D1195797

THE ASSOCIATION FOR SCOTTISH LITERARY STUDIES

NUMBER EIGHT

THE ASSOCIATION FOR SCOTTISH LITERARY STUDIES

GENERAL EDITOR – DAVID BUCHAN

JOHN GALT

SELECTED SHORT STORIES

EDITED BY

IAN A. GORDON

SCOTTISH ACADEMIC PRESS

EDINBURGH

1978

Published by
Scottish Academic Press Ltd
33 Montgomery Street, Edinburgh EH7 5JX

First published 1978
SBN 7073 0218 8

Printed in Great Britain by
R. & R. Clark Ltd, Edinburgh

CONTENTS

INTRODUCTION

Galt's ability to write short stories crept up on him unawares. He was always, in print, a raconteur, a good teller of yarns – short narratives where the lively succession of the incidents rather than the individual quality of the characters was what mattered. When, in the creative burst between 1819 and 1822 that produced the *Annals*, *The Provost* and *The Entail*, he temporararily ran out of material for a full novel, he strung together some of his yarns and incorporated them into *The Steamboat* of 1822. A series of yarns, with or without an enclosing framework, is the essence of such books as *The Bachelor's Wife* of 1824, *My Landlady and her Lodgers*, which he contributed to *Blackwood's Magazine* in 1830, and the gathering of old and new material that made up the three volumes of his *Stories of My Study*, 1833. Scattered among the periodicals, keepsakes and collections of the day – *Blackwood's Magazine*, *Frazer's Magazine*, the *New Monthly Magazine*, *The Literary Souvenir* and Lady Blessington's various productions – are numerous examples of his ability to dash off readable yarns written (as his surviving manuscripts show) with an easy running pen.

What brought Galt to a realisation that there was more to the short story than the simple yarn, was the illness which, from an early warning in 1831, developed into a stroke in the following year, ultimately enforcing his departure from the London scene, after which he made a slow but effective recovery in Greenock. His final novel *Eben Erskine* had been completed for Colburn and Bentley in the latter part of 1832. By the end of that year, and for some months thereafter, Galt's physical condition was such that he could append his name only with difficulty to a memorandum of agreement for the purchase of the copyright of *Lawrie Todd*. He was never going to create another long sustained work. He would never write another novel.

Consciously or unconsciously, Galt settled in this situation on what for him was a new genre, the short story. All the stories collected in this volume were written between 1832 and 1836. They represent, in technique, a new beginning. Thematically, they form a set of retrospective variations on his best work in its longer form. From the

Annals of the Parish he drew, in *The Mem*, yet one more chronicle of Dalmailing; and its ambience – his Irvine birthplace – led to the matching characters in *The Gudewife* and *The Seamstress*. Combining his Irvine boyhood memories with his experience of his publishers, Blackwood and Colburn and Bentley, he produced in manuscript (it is printed in book form here for the first time) the ironic beginning of *The Publisher*. Turning to his other Irvine – the political microcosm of *The Provost* – he wrote *Our Borough*; and he followed this story of small-town life by launching his politician on the current London scene, in a sequel *The Dean of Guild*. (He wrote a further, extended, sequel – politician and wife on an innocents abroad tour through Europe – called *The Jaunt*, which limitations of space have compelled me to omit from this selection.) All of these stories were completed before he left London for Greenock.

Settled in Greenock, he continued with his discovery of the potentialities of the short story. *The Howdie* ('The Midwife') returns to the 'vulgar' Galt of *The Last of the Lairds*. *Tribulations of the Rev. Cowal Kilmun* explores new experiences that border on the surrealistic. *A Rich Man*, a story expanded to novella length and one of the best things Galt ever wrote, is a magnificently ironic progress from rags to riches, echoing, but improving on, the theme of *Sir Andrew Wylie*. The series was brought to a close with a return to the wider political world of *The Member* in a short story cast in the form of a manual of political behaviour entitled *The Statesman*.

The stories reprinted in this volume show that he has abandoned the facile and easily written yarn of his earlier days for a tightly constructed genre that can measure up to the best of his novels. Galt is in firm artistic control of his material and his medium. There is a unity of feeling and of presentation in his portrayal of characters as diverse as Miss Peerie (his schoolmistress), Mrs Blithe (his midwife), and Archibald Plack (his rich man), that remind us of the creator of Micah Balwhidder and of Claud Walkinshaw and the Leddy. Because it demonstrates Galt's seriousness of purpose in his deliberate and considered choice of Scots as his ultimate literary medium, I have retained the introduction he wrote for *The Seamstress*. Galt knew what he was up to.

The outburst of short stories that came in Galt's Indian summer has never achieved critical attention. One is printed from his manuscript and this is its first appearance in book form. Another is reprinted here in its entirety for the first time. A third makes its first appearance here since its printing in 1836. Written, as they were, in the West of Scotland – the spoken language in his ears day and night – they seem to me to transmute into literary form an idiom that is not matched for authenticity and authority even in his better-known novels.

The Publisher and a portion of *The Howdie* are all that survive in manuscript. For the remainder, texts are derived from the first printings. Background information on each of the stories is given in the Notes. Galt wrote a century and a half ago. The scenes he portrays go back another half century. Inevitably he now requires annotation, both for his language and for historical and local detail. I have left the texts unmarred by indication of footnotes. But the final pages of Annotations and Vocabulary (combined into one alphabetical sequence), will, I hope, provide what is required for the reader curious to discover what is going on.

Wellington, 1977 I.A.G.

ACKNOWLEDGEMENT

The Association for Scottish Literary Studies acknowledges the generous financial assistance of the Scottish Arts Council in the publication of this Volume.

THE MEM, OR SCHOOLMISTRESS

FROM THE PAPERS OF THE LATE REV. MICAH BALWHITHER, OF DALMAILING

Miss Peerie, the schoolmistress, was, about sixty years ago, the most beautiful young woman in our town; her father was head-master of the grammar-school, and she excelled every young lady far and near in accomplishments. She danced, but it was only not to appear above human nature; every body who saw her had no adjective which her beauty could be described; Greek and Latin were to her household words, and she could read Hebrew as easily as if it had been the A B C.

She was then blooming: the epithet bonny was never applied to a more suitable subject , and her temper was as mellow as her looks were sweet. She had such a sleight in dressing, that every thing she wore seemed to grow better on her than on any other young lady; and on her every pattern, no matter how old-fashioned, seemed to improve in gaiety and beauty.

But marriages are made in heaven, and fortune is not at man's bidding. Years have passed away, her beauty departed, and her still more delightful temper become all odds and ends, like the contents of a wisdom-bag. Had the boldest soothsayer foretold her fate in that blithesome time, he would have been derided as envious and malignant; nor was it in the heart of man to imagine she would ever become the lonely inhabitant of a garret-room, and exercise the rod of authority over negligent and giggling misses. And yet such came to pass: she lived in an attic, and followed the patient and penurious bread-making of a schoolmistress, until her failing sight obliged her to give up the teaching of white-seam with the hieroglyphicals of the sampler, and to addict herself in the twilight of old age entirely to the knitting of stockings. But the course of life with Miss Peerie, if we except her schoolmistressing, was not uncommon; though the world withholds its sympathy from many that equally deserve it. She was the victim of disappointments, and a low winter sun dawned upon her lot, which through all her days has only served to shew its bleakness.

But I am anticipating the results of a sad and simple tale. I cannot, however, refrain from saying as much when speaking of the sunny days of my youth, and remembering the flowers that bloomed in my path with such loveliness.

The first misfortune that fell on Miss Peerie was the death of her father. He was a learned, erect, and accurate man – the whole presbytery acknowledged that he had not his equal among them for a recondite knowledge of those ancient mysteries, which make many men learned merely by knowing that they were once believed. But, above all, he was celebrated for the method with which he had trasmitted all his lore to his glad and gamboling daughter, his only child, without leading her to imagine that she possessed any talent above her companions.

He died when she was on the threshold of life, and from that moment an increasing blight was evidently upon her. Before her mournings were well worn, the poor widow, her mother, who had never lifted her head from the hour of the master's death, pined away in unspeakable sorrow, and left the orphan exposed to the trials and tribulations of a harsh and hard-hearted world.

But soon after her death, Peter Rattlings, the mate of a ship called the Sea-Flower, which traded to Virginia, made up to Miss Peerie, and promised when he returned to make her his wife: but he never returned. Soon after he sailed, the wind blew, the rain fell, and in a dismal night the gallant Sea-Flower foundered off the Tuscar, when all hands perished.

The sad tidings of this disaster coming on the heels of the loss that the winsome maiden had sustained by the removal of her mother, was a grief that could not be soon mastered. She was so long off laughing in her young manner, that she forgot the way of it; and the rosy hue on her cheek vanished for ever like the sun-beams of the evening, which tinge the pale cloud once and never glow on it again.

Every body in the town sympathised with the poor afflicted Miss Peerie; and ladies in the country, to whom her name till that time was unknown, sent her many a kind present; but she grew more woful and sequestered every day. Some said (as I shall never forget), that grief made her raven locks untimely grey; but it was thought that anxiety was mingled with her sorrow, for when time softened her grief, and bred negligence in those that felt for her distress, she became very poor; and if she had not plucked up a wonderful resolution for one so broken-hearted, she would have outlived the sympathies of all who knew her.

In her extremity, a courage, by common consent, was lent to her; and she consulted Mrs Psalmody, the minister's wife, about taking up a school to earn her crumb. In this matter the lady gave her great heart, and advised her to teach the young ladies of the town to read the Scriptures in Hebrew with the Greek Testament – things which were greatly wanted among them, no one knowing an alpha from a beta; but Miss Peerie herself was more moderate in her ideas, and said to Mrs Psalmody, that as all the young ladies of the burgh were ordained to be men's wives, it would be more conciliatory if she would just undertake to teach them plain work.

Thus it came to pass, upon consulting the minister upon the subject, that Miss Peerie should take up a school of the discreet latter kind, and let it be known that she would give private lessons in Hebrew to those misses that were desirous of reading the Scriptures in the original. Accordingly Miss Peerie took up a school of plain-work, in which she was surely a great teacher; for all the young ladies, gentle and simple, were sent to her school, some to make shirts, others to hem neckcloths and to work stockings, with various items of household drudgery. It said, however, very little for the wisdom of their parents, that not one of the young ladies was sent to learn Hebrew.

Well was it (for thin and pale Miss Peerie was then grown) that the thought was put into her head to take up a school. I remember at the time it was said, that if the provost's lady had not sent with her three daughters a beforehand payment of the school wage, by which a good example was set to other folk, she would not have been able to have fought so bravely with her circumstances; as on the Saturday night before she opened her school, which was on a Monday morning, she had nothing to put in the basin, and was obligated to borrow a handful of meal and a rusted herring to get over the Sabbath day. Her lines, poor thing! had not fallen on pleasant places; but for all that, she received a modicum of human pity, and many that were thought of ne'er-begun dispositions, shed a tear when it was reported that she had been so destitute.

From the time that she took up her school it could not be said that she was in absolute want, for James Plane, the carpenter, told my father in my own hearing that, to his certain knowledge, Miss Peerie was making money, and had a seventeen-pound gathering in the bank; which was wonderful to hear of, as she had been only then one-and-twenty years a schoolmistress. But I should mention, that all the ladies that had been her first scholars made a point of sending their daughters to learn every thing that Miss Peerie taught in public. Once she had, also, two scholars, prejinct misses, the daughters of an Englisher, that had a post in the government about our custom-house, at her private class, learning French (which Miss Peerie taught in the most perfect manner); but their father would not hear of them learning Hebrew or mathematicals, though it was well known that Miss Peerie was as capable of teaching them as any professor in a college.

Well do I recollect when it was known that Miss Peerie had money in the bank, that the story ran about like wildfire, and received from all who spoke of it great augmentation; insomuch, that the very lowest sum any one thought it worth their while to name was hundreds of pounds, and she in consequence was reputed to be a rich and miserly woman; for by this time, as I have said, she was more than forty years of age, and had a pinched and peeping look, as if she stinted herself in the sanctified uses of the necessaries of life. But for all that, the rumour of her wealth spread far and wide, and was not without an effect; for mankind, hearing that she was so bien, laid their heads together concerning her treasure, and sent divers wooers to Miss Peerie because of her purse. She, however, was not to be easily won; only Colin Pennyton was not so soon turned away of his own accord, for he remembered the proverb that says 'faint heart never won fair lady,' and thought by sticking to her he would carry the day.

Of this Colin Pennyton I cannot speak of much of a certainty, from my own knowledge of the man; but he was thirteen years older than Miss Peerie, and had, it was said, a purse of his own, that he could shake in the teeth of a north-east blast. He was in his looks more elderly than those who had been brought up with him said he was; particularly Miss Babby M'Cun, who made a point of telling on all occasions that he was a much younger man than the gossipry of the town would let him be. But Miss Babby's remonstrances were not much heeded, for it was recollected that they were both christened on the same afternoon in the Auld Kirk; which was a plain proof that she had an interest in keeping him young, as she herself was far from despairing of making some honest man's life bitter – for she was, to her latter days, a most controverting woman.

Colin, as we have said, adhered to Miss Peerie with the tenacity of a sticking-plaster; but it would not do: for some day, in the mirk of the night, she had made a vow to live and die in single blessedness, which she did in the most abstemious manner perform; and Colin in the end, seeing he had no hope, gave up his vain pursuit, while Miss Peerie continued to keep a school in unmolested tranquillity.

It happened, however, that notwithstanding she had done all in the power of a prudent and parsimonious person to do, her sphere, little as she made it, could not be considered altogether a nonentity; for she met with rubs, and had her share of misfortunes over and above the great calamities that I have rehearsed. It therefore behoves me to tell the courteous reader, that her way of life was not favourable to the growth of her understanding; for as she waxed older she grew more penurious, and by the time she had reached her fifties she was a meagre sister, and not prized for the capacity of her judgment. But there was a nerve in her that well deserves to be laid open to public commendation, though in the end to herself it was a great loss, and became the parent of many afflictions.

The regular teaching of her school was over on the Saturdays by twelve o'clock, and all the afternoon the scholars had for play, while the Mem was known to be very busy in setting her house in order. She did this in a most excellent manner, and in the doing of it went about the business cannily and cautiously, as became her looks and her character. But one day, when she was in her fifties, she took the rheumatics in her back; and not being able to stoop as she was wont, she became fain to ask some of the biggest lassies to assist her in the Saturday afternoon's thrift. At last it came into her head that she would make house-cleaning one of the tasks of her school, and teach rambling misses how to set about it. Accordingly she enacted that they should in turns do her work for a lesson every Saturday, that they might get an insight of that business.

Thus it was brought to a come-to-pass that she not only spared herself from the toil of rubbing and scrubbing, but got some additional wage for teaching how a house should be cleaned; by which she earned, it was said, a good penny.

When she first gave notice of her intent to make it an edifying branch of education, every mother that had a daughter was delighted with the scheme; and the whole lot of the scholars pressed forward to be taken into what was called the domestic class. The thought, therefore, though begotten of necessity, was, by the natural cleverness of Miss Peerie's thoughtful mind, turned to a profitable account.

It was not, however, all clear profit that she made by it; for either there were too many of the misses at one time employed, by which there was bred anarchy and confusion, or others of them were not so circumspect in the task as they should have been.

Miss Peerie had in her room a dresser, and above that dresser a few shelves, on which she was in the habit of putting her plates on rim, with their faces to the public; making, I will say, a very goodly show, especially when she put before each a knife and fork and well-cleaned pewter spoon, that had been her father's, and for many a year retained by her as an honesty. Upon this dresser there was placed a row of tea-pots, pouries, teacups, and other utensils with handles, making an apparition of great wealth in such sort of things; and the misses, when they set the house in order, never forgot to wash and arrange them: but in doing this, being young heedless creatures, they did not pay that attention to these idols, and the consequence was, that one day when the Mem, as they called her, happened to be on an inspection, she saw with unutterable astonishment that havoc had been busy among these precious vessels. Few of the cups were without flaws or cracks; the teapot-lids were mutilated in their nipples; the noses of the pouries had suffered great damage; and there was a china bowl ruined for ever by a piece broken out of the lip, which the cunning cutties placed with the broken side to the wall.

At first Miss Peerie, greatly grieved at such destruction, examined the last squad, one by one, concerning the calamity. But they all said that the disasters had taken place before their time, and that they had only made the nicest arrangement that was in their power to do, by placing the damaged articles in such a way as to hide their blemishes.

In the examination, Miss Marigold stood up uncalled for, and testified to the truth of this evidence, shewing that the broken bowl must have met with its detriment a long time ago; for if Miss Peerie would examine the edge of the injury she would see the fact, for it was all dirty, as breaks are that have been of a long standing.

Miss Peerie gave heed to her words, and examined the broken bowl; when she saw, sure enough, that the edge of the crack was very dirty, and had an old appearance, as the young lady so philosophically described it should be. But upon looking still closer, she discovered that all the broken edge was not of an equal age, particularly in one part, where an unblemished spot clearly proved to her understanding that the bowl had received its wound very recently: and so, by a cogent process of reasoning, she deducted from the premises that Miss Marigold was art and part in the guilt of the breakage; which, after much questioning, that young lady was forced to confess, and then pay for the damage.

Well do I recollect how Miss Peerie told my mother of this stratagem when I was writing at the scrutoire; and she foretold that this device of Miss Marigold argued no great things for her future conduct. But the most extraordinary accident in her recital was, that she told the machination with a laugh that made my mother afterwards say, 'Miss Peerie was not beyond the efficacy of mirth.'

In the mean time Miss Peerie was waxing old, and growing well stricken in years, to which her frugal and sedentary way offered no obstacle; so that she in time became an old woman bent into a hoop, and leaning upon a staff, with her head bound with a black silk handkerchief, and her apron shewing the folds for days after she had taken it out of them. In truth she was a wonderful woman, from ever after the time that she came to years of discretion and was left friendless on the wide world; to those that considered her case she was something more than common. Indeed, Miss Peerie had in all her days, and especially towards her latter end, been very unlike the generality of the daughters of men, taking her own course quietly in the bypaths of life; and was, to speak truly of her, a woman out of the world and yet in it.

At first her forlorn condition made her constant sadness not remarkable: it seemed, in the opinion of every body, natural and becoming; and though many condoled at the way she lived aloof, none thought that she could be drawn from her retirement. Maybe they were right; but they made no effort, and the poor woman was habituated to neglect long before those that were to blame suspected themselves of committing any wrong towards her. Thus she was far above the thirties before it was thought that the carelessness of her neighbours had been in any degree the cause of her loneliness. She was far advanced in life when it was by-hand noticed, and it had grown into a second nature with her, that would not be altered; but in all the time there was never the slightest tint of imputation against the purity of her behaviour, only when she was grown old people spoke of her conduct as little like that of the common world, and made a marvel of her strangeness, which began in grief and was cherished with melancholy.

Miss Peerie was always a very interesting creature with me, for although she was born in a time that made her much my senior, yet there was a recluse patience about her very unlike the garishness of the world. I never saw her but she made me sorrowful; for her face was pale, and her eyes often so bright, that she had a spirituality sometimes about her that no one could see and withstand, without feeling a melting compassion in his bosom.

In the Sabbath evenings, when all nature was sedate, and the sounds both of the blacksmith's hammer and the wheels of the waggon and market-cart were at rest, Miss Peerie might be seen walking by herself by the river side, or meditating among the whins on the green. As long as I recollect, this was the case. Every one that saw her spoke in passing by, and her words in answer were few and well chosen; but they gave no encouragement to any communion.

Sometimes she took a cup of tea with divers of her acquaintance; but gradually, as if it was a rule she had laid down for herself, she abstained from going to their houses, and they ceased to wonder at her absence.

At last the rheumatics in her legs put an end to her solitary walks, and her narrow course was in consequence confined to her room; where, when the winter raged without, she had a small fire – just a pinch of chips and coals that, to folks used to galravaging, would have made the cold sensible. But she was content with the spunk, and sat alone all night beside it, sometimes with spread hands cowering over the flames, reading a book by the light of her cruise, and heaping up knowledge that it was plain to all that saw her could never be put to use in this world; – in the next, all worldly wisdom is foolishness, as is well known.

One Sunday afternoon, when it was rather rainy, there came on a shower just as I passed her close mouth; and remembering her, I took the benefit of the wet to shelter there. Being constrained to wait longer than I expected, it came into my head to go up stairs and inquire for her. No doubt it was a fool thought of me so to do, for I was but slenderly acquainted with the ailing woman: we knew, however, each other well enough for need to give me the privilege. So I went up the wooden stair. I mind the place; it was very dark, and had a ravel of rope, useful to the lame and the aged in going up and down.

When I had reached her door, instead of rapping with my knuckle before entering, as maybe I should have done, in I went at once, and there was the clean, respectable-looking old woman taking her tea, beside her spark of fire. She had for her table a big stool, with a finger hole in the middle of it; and for her teapot, notwithstanding the grand row on her dresser, she had a coarse, stumpy, brick-coloured commodity, that held enough, no doubt, for one. But when I told her what had driven me in, she invited me to take a cup with her, and the track pot was in consequence obliged that night to serve two; but her tea was very thin, and she had her small condiment of sugar in a tea cup, that shewed nothing was allowed for waste.

After I had solaced myself with her frugal beverage, the rain continuing to blatter on the windows, she made an endeavour to converse with me concerning many things, such as the Trojan war, and Numa Pompilius, a king of Rome, wherein she gave me a sample of the lore that she had learned from her father. But she was not like an earthly creature, for her mind ran on old things, such as the building of the pyramids of Egypt, and Queen Cleopatra, and Isaac and Abraham, the fathers and founders of the Israelitish people.

Saving that accidental visit, which was most interesting, I never had a specimen of the great learning that she inherited from her father. She was, however, a dungeon of wit, and made no brag of what she knew.

Soon after that visit she was constrained to give up her school, and to prepare herself for another and a better world, which made me very woful to hear; for though it could not be said that her life was barren of utility, as she taught the daughters of many mothers thrift and good conduct, it was sad to think that all her days were just a struggle to flee from the fangs of famine.

The only good fortune that befel this innocent creature was that death did not make her latter end a kittle case, but stopped her breath in a sudden cough, when she had no complaint but the pains in her knees and ancles; and fortunately this happened when the misses were coming in the morning to school, so that she did not die unseen, as many feared she would do.

Dreadful was the cry made by her scholars when they saw that she was dead. Some ran home, others to the doctor's shop; but it was all in vain – the unblemished soul of Miss Peerie had taken the wings of the morning and flown away into Abraham's bosom. Great was the lamentation that ensued. Mothers wondered what they would do with their daughters, and really were in as great an affliction as if they all had been marriageable. However, their grief was not of a durable nature, and was soon forgotten when Miss Peerie was laid in the churchyard. But still she has been a mystery to me. For what use was knowledge and instruction given to her? I ponder when I think of it, but have no answer to the question.

THE GUDEWIFE

Introduction

I am inditing the good matter of this book for the instruction of our only daughter when she comes to years of discretion, as she soon will, for her guidance when she has a house of her own, and has to deal with the kittle temper of a gudeman in so couthy a manner as to mollify his sour humour when any thing out of doors troubles him. Thanks be and praise I am not ill qualified! indeed, it is a clear ordinance that I was to be of such a benefit to the world; for it would have been a strange thing if the pains taken with my education had been purposeless in the decrees of Providence.

Mr Desker, the schoolmaster, was my father; and, as he was reckoned in his day a great teacher, and had a pleasure in opening my genie for learning, it is but reasonable to suppose that I in a certain manner profited by his lessons, and made a progress in parts of learning that do not fall often into the lot of womankind. This much it behoves me to say, for there are critical persons in the world that might think it was very upsetting of one of my degree to write a book, especially a book which has for its end the bettering of the conjugal condition. If I did not tell them, as I take it upon me to do, how well I have been brought up for the work, they might look down upon my endeavours with a doubtful eye; but when they read this, they will have a new tout to their old horn, and reflect with more reverence of others who may be in some things their inferiors, superiors, or equals. It would not become me to say to which of these classes I belong, though I am not without an inward admonition on that head.

It fell out, when I was in my twenties, that Mr Thrifter came, in the words of the song of Auld Robin Gray, 'a-courting to me'; and, to speak a plain matter of fact, in some points he was like that bald-headed carle. For he was a man, considering my juvenility, well stricken in years; besides being a bachelor, with a natural inclination (as all old bachelors have) to be dozened, and fond of his own ayes and nays. For my part, when he first came about the house, I was as dawty as Jeanie – as I thought myself entitled to a young man, and did not relish the apparition of him coming in at the gloaming, when the day's darg was done, and before candles were lighted. However, our lot in life is not of our own choosing. I will say – for he is still to the fore – that it could not have been thought he would have proved himself such a satisfactory gudeman as he has been. To be sure, I put my shoulder to the wheel, and likewise prayed to Jupiter; for there never was a rightful head of a family without the concurrence of his wife. These are words of wisdom that my father taught, and I put in practice.

Mr Thrifter, when he first came about me, was a bein man. He had parts in two vessels, besides his own shop, and was sponsible for a nest-egg of lying money: so that he was not, though rather old, a match to be, as my father thought, discomfited with a flea in the lug instanter. I therefore, according to the best advice, so comported myself, that it came to pass in the course of time that we were married; and of my wedded life and experience I intend to treat in this book.

Chapter I

Among the last words that my sagacious father said when I took upon me to be the wedded wife of Mr Thrifter were, that a man never throve unless his wife would let, which is a text that I have not forgotten; for though in a way, and in obedience to the customs of the world, women acknowledge men as their head, yet we all know in our hearts that this is but diplomatical. Do not we see that men work for us, which shews that they are our servants? do not we see that men protect us, are they not therefore our soldiers? do not we see that they go hither and yon at our bidding, which shews that they have that within their nature that teaches them to obey? and do not we feel that we have the command of them in all things, just as they had the upper hand in the world till woman was created? No clearer proof do I want that, although in a sense for policy we call ourselves the weaker vessels – and in that very policy there is power – we know well in our hearts that, as the last made creatures, we necessarily are more perfect, and have all that was made before us, by hook or crook, under our thumb. Well does Robin Burns sing of this truth in the song where he has –

> Her 'prentice hand she tried on man,
> And syne she made the lassies oh!

Accordingly having a proper conviction of the superiority of my sex, I was not long of making Mr Thrifter, my gudeman, to know into what hands he had fallen, by correcting many of the bad habits of body to which he had become addicted in his bachelor loneliness. Among these was a custom that I did think ought not to be continued after he had surrendered himself into the custody of a wife, and that was an usage with him in the morning before breakfast to toast his shoes against the fender and forenent the fire. This he did not tell me till I saw it with my own eyes the morning after we were married, which when I beheld gave me a sore heart, because, had I known it before we were everlastingly made one, I will not say but there might have been a dubiety as to the paction; for I have ever had a natural dislike to men who toasted their shoes, thinking it was a hussie fellow's custom. However, being endowed with an instinct of prudence, I winked at it for some days; but it could not be borne any longer, and I said in a sweet manner, as it were by the by,

'Dear Mr Thrifter, that servant lass that we have gotten has not a right notion of what is a genteel way of living. Do you see how the misleart creature sets up your shoes in the inside of the fender, keeping the warmth from our feet? really I'll thole this no longer; it's not a custom in a proper house. If a stranger were accidentally coming in and seeing your shoes in that situation, he would not think of me as it is well known he ought to think.'

Mr Thrifter did not say much, nor could he; for I judiciously laid all the wyte and blame of the thing to the servant; but he said, in a diffident manner, that it was not necessary to be so particular.

'No necessary! Mr Thrifter, what do you call a particularity, when you would say that toasting shoes is not one? It might do for you when you were a bachelor, but ye should remember that you're so no more, and its a custom I will not allow.'

'But,' replied he with a smile, 'I am the head of the house; and, to make few words about it, I say, Mrs Thrifter, I will have my shoes warmed any how, whether or no.'

'Very right, my dear,' quo' I; 'I'll ne'er dispute that you are the head of the house; but I think that you need not make a poor wife's life bitter by insisting on toasting your shoes.'

And I gave a deep sigh. Mr Thrifter looked very solemn on hearing this, and as he was a man not void of understanding, he said to me.

'My dawty,' said he, 'we must not stand on trifles; if you do not like to see my shoes within the parlour fender, they can be toasted in the kitchen.'

I was glad to hear him say this; and, ringing the bell, I told the servant-maid at once to take them away and place them before the kitchen-fire, well pleased to have carried my point with such debonair suavity; for if you get the substance of a thing, it is not wise to make a piece of work for the shadow likewise. Thus it happened I was conqueror in the controversy; but Mr Thrifter's shoes have to this day been toasted every morning in the kitchen; and I daresay the poor man is vogie with the thoughts of having gained a victory; for the generality of men have, like parrots, a good conceit of themselves, and cry 'Pretty Poll!' when every body sees they have a crooked neb.

Chapter II

But what I have said was nothing to may other calamities that darkened our honeymoon. Mr Thrifter having been a long-keepit bachelor, required a consideration in many things besides his shoes; for men of that stamp are so long accustomed to their own ways, that it is not easy to hammer them into docility, far less to make them obedient husbands. So that although he is the best of men, yet I cannot say on my conscience that he was altogether free of an ingrained temper, requiring my canniest hand to manage properly. It could not be said that I suffered much from great faults; but he was fiky, and made more work about trifles that didna just please him that I was willing to conform to. Some excuse, however, might be pleaded for him, because he felt that infirmities were growing upon him, which was the cause that made him think of taking a wife; and I was not in my younger days quite so thoughtful, may be, as was necessary: for I will take blame to myself, when it would be a great breach of truth in me to deny a fault that could be clearly proven.

Mr Thrifter was a man of great regularity; he went to the shop, and did his business there in a most methodical manner; he returned to the house and ate his meals like clockwork; and he went to bed every night at half-past nine o'clock, and slept there like a door-nail. In short, all he did and said was as orderly as commodities on chandler-pins; but for all that, he was at times of a crunkly spirit, fractiously making faults about nothing at all: by which he was neither so smooth as oil nor so sweet as honey to me, whose duty it was to govern him.

At the first outbreaking of the original sin that was in him, I was vexed and grieved, watering my plants in the solitude of my room, when he was discoursing on the news of the day with customers in the shop. At last I said to myself, 'This will never do; one of two must obey: and it is not in the course of nature that a gudeman should rule a house, which is the province of a wife, and becomes her nature to do.'

So I set a stout heart to the steybrae, and being near my time with our daughter, I thought it would be well to try how he would put up with a little sample of womanhood. So that day when he came in to his dinner, I was, maybe, more incommoded with my temper than might be, saying to him, in a way as if I could have fought with the wind, that it was very unsettled weather.

'My dawty,' said he, 'I wonder what would content you! we have had as delightful a week as ever made the sight of the sun heartsome.'

'Well, but,' said I, 'good weather that is to you may not be so to me; and I say again, that this is most ridiculous weather.'

'What would you have, my dawty? Is it not known by a better what is best for us?'

'Oh,' cried I, 'we can never speak of temporal things but you haul in the grace of the Maker by the lug and the horn. Mr Thrifter, ye should set a watch on the door of your lips; especially as ye have now such a prospect before you of being the father of a family.'

'Mrs Thrifter,' said he, 'what has that to do with the state of the weather?'

'Every thing,' said I. 'Isn't the condition that I am in a visibility that I cannot look after the house as I should do? which is the cause of your having such a poor dinner to-day; for the weather wiled out the servant lass, and she has in consequence not been in the kitchen to see to her duty. Doesn't that shew you that, to a woman in the state that I am, fine sunshiny weather is no comfort?'

'Well,' said he, 'though a shower is at times seasonable, I will say that I prefer days like this.'

'What you, Mr Thrifter, prefer, can make no difference to me; but I will uphold, in spite of every thing you can allege to the contrary, that this is not judicious weather.'

'Really now, gudewife,' said Mr Thrifter, 'what need we quarrel about the weather? neither of us can make it better or worse.'

'That's a truth,' said I; 'but what need you maintain that dry weather is pleasant weather, when I have made it plain to you that it is a great affliction? And how can you say the contrary? does not both wet and dry come from Providence? Which of them is the evil? – for they should be in their visitations both alike.'

"Mrs Thrifter,' said he, 'what would you be at, summering and wintering on nothing?'

Upon which I said, 'Oh, Mr Thrifter, if ye were like me, ye would say any thing; for I am not in a condition to be spoken to. I'll not say that ye're far wrong, but till my time is a bygone ye should not contradict me so; for I am no in a state to be contradicted: it may go hard with me if I am. So I beg you to think, for the sake of the baby unborn, to let me have my own way in all things for a season.'

'I have no objection,' said he, 'if there is a necessity for complying; but really, gudewife, ye're at times a wee fashous just now; and this house has not been a corner in the kingdom of heaven for some time.'

Thus, from less to more, our argolbargoling was put an end to; and from that time I was the ruling power in our domicile, which has made it the habitation of quiet ever since; for from that moment I never laid down the rod of authority, which I achieved with such a womanly sleight of hand.

Chapter III

Though from the time of the conversation recorded in the preceding chapter I was, in a certain sense, the ruling power in our house, as a wedded wife should be, we did not slide down a glassy brae till long after. For though the gudeman in a compassionate manner allowed me to have my own way till my fulness of time was come, I could discern by the tail of my eye that he meditated to usurp the authority again, when he saw a fit time to effect the machination. Thus it came to pass, when I was delivered of our daughter, I had, as I lay on my bed, my own thoughts anent the evil that I saw barming within him; and I was therefore determined to keep the upper hand, of which I had made a conquest with such dexterity, and the breaking down of difficulties.

So when I was some days in a recumbent posture, but in a well-doing way, I said nothing; it made me, however, often grind my teeth in a secrecy, when I saw from the bed many a thing that I treasured in remembrance should never be again. But I was very thankful for my deliverance, and assumed a blitheness in my countenance that was far from my heart. In short, I could see that the gudeman, in whose mouth you would have thought sugar would not have melted, had from day to day a stratagem in his head subversive of the regency that I had won in my tender state; and as I saw it would never do to let him have his own will, I had recourse to the usual diplomaticals of womankind.

It was a matter before the birth that we settled, him and me, that the child should be baptised on the eighth day after, in order that I might be up, and a partaker of the ploy; which, surely, as the mother, I was well entitled to. But from what I saw going on from the bed and jaloused, it occurred to me that the occasion should be postponed, and according as Mr Thrifter should give his consent, or withhold it, I should comport myself; determined, however, I was to have the matter postponed, just to ascertain the strength and durability of what belonged to me.

On the fifth day I therefore said to him, as I was sitting in the easy chair by the fire, with a cod at my shoulders and my mother's fur-cloak about me – the baby was in the cradle close by, but not rocking, for the keeper said it was yet too young – and sitting as I have said, Mr Thrifter forenent me,

'My dear,' said I, 'it will never do to have the christening on the day we said.'

'What for no?' was the reply; 'isn't it a very good day?'

So I, seeing that he was going to be upon his peremptors, replied, with my usual meekness,

'No human being, my dear, can tell what sort of day it will be; but be it good or be it bad, the christening is not to be on that day.'

'You surprise me!' said he. 'I considered it a settled point, and have asked Mr Sweetie, the grocer, to come to his tea.'

'Dear me!' quo' I; 'ye should not have done that without my consent; for although we set the day before my time was come, it was not then in the power of man to say how I was to get through; and therefore it was just a talk we had on the subject, and by no manner of means a thing that could be fixed.'

'In some sort,' said Mr Thrifter, 'I cannot but allow that you are speaking truth; but I thought that the only impediment to the day was your illness. Now you have had a most blithe time o't, and there is nothing in the way of an obstacle.'

'Ah, Mr Thrifter!' said I, 'it's easy for you, who have such a barren knowledge of the nature of women, so to speak, but I know that I am no in a condition to have such a handling as a christening; and besides, I have a scruple of conscience well worth your attention concerning the same – and its my opinion, formed in the watches of the night, when I was in my bed, that the baby should be christened in the kirk on the Lord's-day.'

'Oh,' said he, 'that's but a fashion, and you'll be quite well by the eighth; the howdie told me that ye had a most pleasant time o't, and cannot be ill on the eighth day.'

I was just provoked into contumacy to hear this; for to tell a new mother that childbirth is a pleasant thing, set me almost in a passion; and I said to him, that he might entertain Mr Sweetie himself, for that I was resolved the christening should not be as had been set.

In short, from less to more I gained my point; as, indeed, I always settled it in my own mind before broaching the subject; first, by letting him know that I had latent pains, which made me very ill, though I seemed otherwise; and, secondly, that it was very hard, and next to a martyrdom, to be controverted in religion, as I would be if the bairn was baptised any where but in the church.

Chapter IV

In due time the christening took place in the kirk, as I had made a point of having; and for some time after we passed a very happy married life. Mr Thrifter saw that it was of no use to contradict me, and in consequence we lived in great felicity, he never saying nay to me; and I, as became a wife in the rightful possession of her prerogatives, was most condescending. But still he shewed, when he durst, the bull-horn; and would have meddled with our householdry, to the manifest detriment of our conjugal happiness, had I not continued my interdict in the strictest manner. In truth, I was all the time grievously troubled with nursing Nance, our daughter, and could not take the same pains about things that I otherwise would have done; and it is well known that husbands are like mice, that know when the cat is out of the house, or her back turned, they take their own way: and I assure the courteous reader, to say no ill of my gudeman, that he was one of the mice genus.

But at last I had a trial, that was not to be endured with such a composity as if I had been a black snail. It came to pass that our daughter was to be weaned, and on the day settled – a Sabbath-day – we had, of course, much to do, for it behoved in this ceremony that I should keep out of sight; and keeping out of sight, it seemed but reasonable, considering his parentage to the wean, that Mr Thrifter should take my place. So I said to him in the morning, that he must do so, and keep Nance for that day; and, to do the poor man justice, he consented at once, for he well knew that it would come to nothing to be contrary.

So I went to the kirk, leaving him rocking the cradle and singing hush, ba! as he saw need. But oh, dule! scarcely had I left the house when the child screamed up in a panic, and would not be pacified. He thereupon lifted it out of the cradle, and with it in his arms went about the house; but it was such a roaring buckie, that for a long time he was like to go distracted. Over what ensued I draw the curtain, and must only say, that when I came from the church, there he was, a spectacle, and as sour as a crab-apple, blaming me for leaving him with such a devil.

I was really woful to see him, and sympathised in the most pitiful manner with him, on account of what had happened; but the more I condoled with him the more he would not be comforted, and for all my endeavours to keep matters in a propriety, I saw my jurisdiction over the house was in jeopardy; and every now and then the infant cried out, just as if it had been laid upon a heckle. Oh! such a day as that was for Mr Thrifter, when he heard the tyrant bairn shrieking like mad, and every now and then drumming with its wee feetie like desperation, he cried,

'For the love of God, give it a drop of the breast! or it will tempt me to wring off its ancles or its head.'

But I replied composedly that it could not be done, for the wean must be speant, and what he advised was evendown nonsense.

'What has come to pass, both my mother and other sagacious carlines told me I had to look for; and so we must bow the head of resignation to our lot. You'll just,' said I, 'keep the bairn this afternoon; it will not be a long fashery.'

He said nothing, but gave a deep sigh.

At this moment, the bells of the kirk were ringing for the afternoon's discourse, and I lifted my bonnet to put it on and go; but ere I knew where I was, Mr Thrifter was out of the door and away, leaving me alone with the torment in the cradle, which the bells at that moment wakened: and it gave a yell that greatly discomposed me.

Once awa and aye awa, Mr Thrifter went into the fields, and would not come back when I lifted the window and called to him, but walked faster and faster, and was a most demented man; so that I was obligated to stay at home, and would have had my own work with the termagant baby, if my mother had not come in and advised me to give it sweetened rum and water for a pacificator.

Chapter V

Mr Thrifter began in time to be a very complying husband, and we had, after the trial of the weaning, no particular confabulation; indeed he was a very reasonable man, and had a rightful instinct of the reverence that is due to the opinion of a wife of discernment. I do not think, to the best of my recollection, that between the time Nance was weaned till she got her walking shoes and was learning to walk, that we had a single controversy; nor can it be said that we had a great ravelment on that occasion. Indeed, saving our daily higling about trifles not worth remembering, we passed a pleasant life. But when Nance came to get her first walking shoes that was a catastrophe well worthy of being rehearsed for her behoof now.

It happened that for some months before, she had, in place of shoes, red worsted socks; but as she began, from the character of her capering, to kithe that she was coming to her feet, I got a pair of yellow slippers for her; and no mother could take more pains that I did to learn her how to handle her feet. First I tried to teach her to walk by putting a thimble or an apple beyond her reach, at least a chair's breadth off; and then I endeavoured to make the cutty run from me to her father, across the hearth, and he held out his hands to catch her.

This, it will be allowed, was to us pleasant pastime. But it fell out one day, when we were diverting ourselves by making Nance run to and fro between us across the hearth, that the glaiket baudrons chanced to see the seal of her father's watch glittering, and, in coming from him to me, she drew it after her, as if it had been a turnip. He cried, 'Oh, Christal and –' I lifted my hands in wonderment; but the tottling creature, with no more sense than a sucking turkey, whirled the watch, the Almighty knows how! into the fire, and giggled as if she had done an exploit.

'Take it out with the tongs,' said I.

'She's an ill-brought-up wean,' cried he.

The short and the long of it was, before the watch could be got out, the heat broke the glass and made the face of it dreadful; besides, he wore a riband chain – that was in a bleeze before we could make a redemption.

When the straemash was over, I said to him that he could expect no better by wearing his watch in such a manner.

'It is not,' said he, 'the watch that is to blame, but your bardy bairn, that ye have spoiled in the bringing up.'

'Mr Thrifter,' quo' I, 'this is not a time for upbraiding; for if ye mean to insinuate any thing to my disparagement, it is what I will not submit to.'

'E'en as you like, my dawty,' said he; 'but what I say is true – that your daughter will just turn out a randy like her mother.'

'What's that ye say?' quo' I, and I began to wipe my eyes with the corner of my shawl – saying in a pathetic manner, 'If I am a randy, I ken who has made me one.'

'Ken,' said he, 'ken! every body kens that ye are like a clubby foot, made by the hand of God, and passed the remede of doctors.'

Was not this most diabolical to hear? Really my corruption rose at such blasphemy; and starting from my seat, I put my hands on my haunches, and gave a stamp with my foot that made the whole house dirl: 'What does the man mean?' said I.

But he replied with a composity as if he had been in liquor, saying, with an ill-faured smile, 'Sit down, my dawty; you'll do yourself a prejudice if ye allow your passion to get the better of you.'

Could mortal woman thole the like of this; it stunned me speechless, and for a time I thought my authority knocked on the head. But presently the spirit that was in my nature mustered courage, and put a new energy within me, which caused me to say nothing, but to stretch out my feet, and stiffen back, with my hands at my sides, as if I was a dead corpse. Whereupon the good man ran for a tumbler of water to jaup on my face; but when he came near me in this posture, I dauded the glass of water in his face, and drummed with my feet and hands in a delirious manner, which convinced him that I was going by myself. Oh, but he was in an awful terrification! At last, seeing his fear and contrition, I began to moderate, as it seemed; which made him as softly and kindly as if I had been a true frantic woman; which I was not, but a practiser of the feminine art, to keep the ruling power.

Thinking by my state that I was not only gone daft, but not without the need of a soothing, he began to ask my pardon in a proper humility, and with a most pitiful penitence. Whereupon I said to him, that surely he had not a right knowledge of my nature: and then he began to confess a fault, and was such a dejected man, that I took the napkin from my eyes and gave a great guffaw, telling him that surely he was silly daft and gi'en to pikerry, if he thought he could daunton me. 'No, no, Mr Thrifter,' quo' I, 'while I live, and the iron tongs are by the chumly lug, never expect to get the upper hand of me.'

From that time he was as bidable a man as any reasonable woman could desire; but he gave a deep sigh, which was a testificate to me that the leaven of unrighteousness was still within him, and might break out into treason and rebellion if I was not on my guard.

THE SEAMSTRESS

Besides the beautiful inflexions which help to make the idiomatic differences between the languages of Scotland and England, the former possesses many words which have a particular signification of their own, as well as what may be called the local meaning which they derive from the juxta-position in which they may happen to be placed with repect to others. Owing to this peculiarity, the nation has produced, among the lower classes, several poets, who, in the delicate use of phraseology, equal the most refined students of other countries. Indeed, it is the boast of Scotland, that in the ploughman Burns, she has produced one who, in energy of passion and appropriate expression, has had no superior. No doubt something may be due to the fortunate circumstance of the Scotch possessing the whole range of the English language, as well as their own, by which they enjoy an uncommonly rich vocabulary, and, perhaps, the peculiarity to which we are alluding may have originated in this cause. For example, the English have but the word 'industry', to denote that constant patience of labour which belongs equally to rough and moderate tasks; but the Scots have also 'eydency', with its derivatives, descriptive of the same constancy and patience, in employments of a feminine and sedentary kind. We never say a ditcher or a drudger is eydent; but the spinster at her wheel, or the seamstress at her sewing, are eydent; and to illustrate a genuine case of industry free from labour, as we conceive eydency to be, we have recourse to a reminiscence of our youth, in itself at once simple, interesting, and pathetic.

Miss Peggy Pingle lived by herself, on the same flat or floor of an old-fashioned, respectable house, in the royal borough of Stourie. A minister's widow, who had but Sir Harry's fund* for her jointure, occupied the domicile on the other side of the common stair.

Miss Peggy's apartments consisted of a small back chamber, her own room, and a front kitchen, as it must be called from the character of the furniture, though, for the uncarpeted tidiness, it might have been compared to any parlour. The only thing for which it was remarkable was a hospitable-looking roasting-jack, which for many years had been in a state of widowhood, not being called to perform the purposes of its creation for a long period. There was also a dresser, which aspired to the rank of a side board; but, like all vulgar things, its original condition could not be disguised by its assumed gentility. It was ornamented with various articles of porcelain, so arranged that handless pouries endeavoured to conceal the defects of spoutless tea-pots with nippleless lids.

Miss Peggy herself was rather on the go, with small piercing eyes of a light-grey colour; not particular generous in her attitudes, being habitually inclined to draw her elbows close to her sides – speaking with her lips so drawn together that her dainty words were squeezed into a lisp. She had been in her youth the daughter of a respectable gauger, who had but his pay to live on, and who dying young, left Miss Peggy and her mother in very straitened circumstances, insomuch that the meek and illess maiden had to make the needle her bread-winner, and her mother the spinning-wheel serve all the purpose of a pacing-horse, as the song sings in 'My Jo Janet.'

In the course of nature, old Mrs Pingle, who had long been in a peaking and pining way, went out of the world; and Miss Peggy's great eydency to convert her time into a livelihood, began to be observed by her neighbours. Those stirring and full-handed matrons among them, who saw she worked with a smaller candle, and rose earlier after her mother's death, naturally concluded that she had suffered, by the event, some new stinting in her narrow means and, by a kind-hearted hypocrisy, often invited her to take tea with them, saying, 'It need na be a breach in your eydency, so be sure and bring

* The late excellent and Reverend Sir Harry Moncrieff, who for so many years made the hearts of ministers' widows glad by his judicious superintendence of their pensions. [Note by Galt.]

your seam;' and their ramplor children were not less kind to slipping Miss Peggy, whom one of the audacious boys used to call her, and described her as speaking always with a corriander sweetie in her mouth, or the end of the thread with which she had last punctured the eye of her needle.

Day after day was with Miss Pingle as the to-day is like the yesterday – twins could not more resemble each other. The only difference perceptible in her condition was produced by the season. She had heard from her father that, on the 10th of October, fires were lit for the winter in the Excise-office, and extinguished there, for the summer, on the 5th of April, without consulting the weather; and the routine of office was as faithfully observed by the frugal Seamstress, as if it had been ordained, and as unavoidable as the four-and-twenty hours are separated into day and night.

In the coldest days, after the 5th of April, Miss Peggy was seen plying her needle with a blue beak and a pellucid jewel at it; and on the warmest, after the 10th of October, her meagre arms were swaddled with the wonted black worsted mittens. The only irregularity in the pure flow of her rill of life, was from the lengthening and shortening of the days; but she attained at last to such precision on this subject, that she could foretel on what distant day, hour, and minute, candles should be lighted with the least waste of what she called the convience.

It, therefore, does not require any argument to prove that Miss Peggy was a creature ordained for eydency – not one of those rough and bustling individuals who belong to the industrious class; and the whole trickling current of her obscure sequestered life illustrates this truth.

Her father, as we have mentioned, being restricted to a narrow income, his regular salary, her mother was obliged by all expedient means to make the guinea gild as large a surface as possible. Accordingly, Miss Peggy was brought up in the frugalest economy of pinched gentility; and as her father died young, she was obliged, along with her mother, to maintain as it were the same station with contracted means, or, more properly, with no other means that the most commendable assiduity, namely, the matron constantly at her weary wheel, and our heroine with her unwearied needle.

We make this important distinction between the wheel and the needle, because, although we have often overheard malcontent murmurings against the former, yet we do not recollect, in any one instance, the latter spoken of either with complaint or disparagement.

Miss Peggy Pingle being thus obliged, by what statesmen call the exigences of her position, to be as sedentary as a judge, without a *dies non*, except Sunday, was necessarily not exposed to the temptations of life. She never had leisure for gallanting with persons of her own age. The garrish damsels with whom, in her youth, she might have been expected to associate, were all to her as innocent as daffodils in a parterre; and the young men as the inaccessible rose-trees, that are best and least dangerous when seen afar off. In consequence, she reached nearly the years of discretion unobserved by the male sex – a time of life that all the ladies of our acquaintance, under thirty, say is the years between thirty and forty; we once, however, heard a dowager of four-score-and-six confess that the rule was not universal, as she had not then reached the happy period. However, without attempting to determine this uncertain point, it came to pass that Miss Peggy reached her thirty-sixth year and upwards. She was, in fact, what they call in the west of Scotland, where they cultivate a peculiar vernacular, a Dumbarton youth, before she had any reason to suspect that she was not in the kingdom of Heaven, or the kirkgate of Irvine, where there is neither marrying nor giving in marriage.

At that period Dominie Loofie found himself in want of a spouse, and having heard it said that, no doubt, Miss Peggy had a sparing, went to her, and declared his ardent passion, one Saturday afternoon. She intreated him, with many endeavours to appear languishing, that he would spare her blushes till Monday night, that she might have time to consult her friends, whether she ought to marry at all, assuring him if they advised her to change her life, there was not another of the male speshy on who she would so cordially bestow her hand.

One sees in this transaction all the delicacy of one marked out by destiny to give the world an example of eydency. There was an assurance to the Dominie that, as far as Miss Peggy was herself concerned, there could be no doubt that his suit was highly acceptable; the only thing suspicious lay in the application for the opinion of friends, which was not alarming; who having ever heard that any friend dissuaded a lady rather long kept from endeavouring to fulfil the essential purposes of her creation.

It happened, however, that in this case a difficulty arose, which was not foreseen, and which proved fatal: all Miss Peggy's kith and kin highly approved of the match, and no obstacle was visible, only the minister of the parish being afar off, a cousin advised her to see that 'all the law papers anent the matrimony were clear; for at your time of life,' said he, 'matrimony, Miss Peggy, must be a matter of money; and, therefore, I advise you to look well to number one.'

Miss Peggy, accordingly, at the time appointed, communicated the unanimous opinion of her friends to the schoolmaster, who was delighted at the bliss in prospect, and quoted to her a passage from Ovid's Art of Love, in Latin, which the lady just remarked was most pretty to those who knew the signification. But when she spoke of the settlement, the corners of his mouth fell down, and taking up his hat, he went away, saying, very dryly, that he never could endure a woman who, in such a tender crisis, could think of such a sordid topic. The marriage was accordingly broken off; and Miss Peggy resolved on a life of single-blessedness, often declaring an admonishment to young widows, overly anxious to make themselves agreeable, that the masculine gender were perjured wretches, and no woman, but from a sense of duty, would countenance above one in her lifetime.

After the perjury of Dominie Loofie, Miss Peggy Pingle was the most exemplary of her sex. At first she deemed it advisable, being so crossed in love, to take to her bed; but, even in the most dolorous posture, her eydency was conspicuous. When any of the neighbours came in to solace her, and to speak of the great trial she had come through, she could only mope in a melancholy manner, patching her discourse with appropriate texts of Scripture; but, when left alone, the time sometimes hung heavy on her hands, and, to lighten the wings of its flight, she had a seam at the end of her pillow, next the wall, with which she amused herself, as young ladies of quality are said to do, by playing sentimental airs on lute or harp, when they have cause to be in the same disconsolate condition; which, to be sure, is not often, especially if they have plenty of money.

When a decorous space of time had elapsed, Miss Peggy resumed her seat and seam at the window, and although she had met with, as she confessed to many occasional visitors, what would stick to her heart for the term of her life, it was not required that she should go about, making a moan of widowhood, though the needle was really ordained to be her bread-winner.

It is true, that corrupt human nature sometimes got the better of resignation; and Miss Peggy, in her endeavours to forget the false-hearted Dominie, began, as she grew older, to accept invitations to share the ploys and pastimes of young parties; but, at them all, she ever plied her thrift, which had grown into a habitude; for she remembered on such occasions, as she often said herself, the day when she was not always such a staid woman as she then appeared, or had ever seemed since the time of her purloined affections – remarks which she frequently made when she had hardened the ends of her thread in the candle, to make it go through the needle-eye with more agility.

At last Miss Peggy became well stricken in years, and her legs rheumatized, by which she was obliged to remain at home, especially in the cold, or wet nights of winter; but her eydency suffered no abatement. In consequence, however, of being necessarily much alone, she acquired a competent knowledge of the phenomena of nature, as they were developed around her. She could tell the character of the weather without, by the dim, bright, or blazy aspect of the spark in her grate, that serve to make the cold more sensible; and could read the omens which made her penurious candle oracular, in the burning 'tow-wicks, dipped in the fat of Pharaoh's lean kine,' as the huxter, who supplied her, used to say, with a wink, and the special orders of Miss Peggy Pingle.

Sometimes we thought her singularly interesting, and her prognostications from the combustion visible to the naked eye in her grate, were highly so; but her boding candle often displayed more signs of dread advents about to ensue than make the dismal lights mystical that enhance the glory about the cenotaphs of dead kings.

'Do you see that spangle upon the wick,' Miss Peggy has said, 'burning as clear as the eye of a lighthouse? – that betokens a letter from a far friend; if it kithes bright to you, like the morning star, there will be blithe tidings; but if red and grim, like a collegener's bowit in a kirk yard, down on your knees and make your shrift to *The Maker*.' If the neglected snuff were become as mushroom-like as the Premier's wicks at a cabinet dinner, Miss Peggy was sure that a come-to-pass was not far off; and a curl of the grease, as it was turned out or in, was a winding-sheet that foretold the exit of a friend or a foe.

But pyrology was her most especially science: she could divine, when embers were red and yellow, that sailor's wives, with close-drawn hoods, would restless walk the shore; when bright, that coldrife lovers would cuddle together; and, when flame broke lambent from the coal that kechling gossips were with secret.

But Miss Peggy was then waxing old;

> When the sunset of life gives its mystical lore,
> And coming events cast their shadows before;

and, though her needle seemed untired in its speed, she sometimes caught with it the skin of her finger instead of the linen; and her seams, instead of the spotlessness of former years, were often stained with blood – emblems of coffin-nails and burial sugar biscuits, and of the fulness of time when it was appointed she should be gathered to her fathers; but, even then, the considerate spirit of eydence was seen.

Well do we recollect the making of her testament; indeed, though then only in our teens, we were much in the confidence of Miss Peggy, and acted as her chamber council on that occasion.

She had the table set out; and we attended by appointment. Besides materials for writing, she had prepared divers pieces of paper, of different sizes, to represent the different legacies she intended to bequeath; and, having seated herself opposite to us, she gathered them towards her, and began. But, as the making of a will is a very solemn undertaking, before she commenced the dictation her heart filled full, and the tears, for some time, flowed from her eyes; at last, becoming more composed, she began.

After the usual preamble, which we executed in the most approved fashion, being then a sharp lad in a lawyer's office, she proceeded; and having, in due course of law, forgiven all her enemies, which, indeed, was soon done, for I never heard she had one; and, having directed her just debts to be all paid, for she did not owe a farthing, she gave the most particular orders about her funeral; then, she had recourse to the bits of papers, and from them drew the remembrance of those legacies and testimonies of regard on which she had long meditated. Among them, she bequeathed to us a double bottle with two necks, which she recollected we had admired in her cupboard when a boy.

At the conclusion of the ceremonial, and when all the papers were exhausted, she gave a deep sigh, and said that it behoved her to make a clau' respecting the residuary legatee; and she appointed Dominie Loofie, as she said tenderly, 'for auld lang syne.' I did not doubt, as the other bequests were not extravagant, that she had left him a good penny; and, after the interment, he certainly got well on to two pounds.

When the will was made, she placed her domicile in order; and, soon after, took to bed, and departed this life, as she had lived, in the most methodical and quiet manner, her dead clothes being found in one corner of her drawers tied up together, with the will, which we had assisted in framing, pinned in such a manner to the parcel that it could not be missed. The minister himself said at the dirgie, that he did not think that a more prejinct creature had been in the world since the days of Martha mentioned in scripture.

THE PUBLISHER

I

It is not known to the general world what publishers are obliged to indure in the course of their dealings with that most irritable and self-conceited race, the authors of books; and therefore I intend for the benefit of the trade and the instruction of mankind to devote a portion of that leisure, which I have been enabled – thank God – to acquire by my judicious handling as a bookseller, to the elucidating of the subject. In doing this it will be needful to set down something of my own particular history, but I will be as sparing as possible for two reasons. First, because a man who has spent the prime of his days in the regularity of a shop in the Row cannot have met with many notable adventures, and second because the matters of which I purpose to speak are of a nature in which rumination ought to be worthy of attention as events. To say nothing of the very great objection that I, in common with all very sensible persons, have to notifying dramatic affairs.

It might be supposed, considering its high importance to the republic of letters, to which surely both publishers and ordinary booksellers belong, as well as hawkers of ballads and the dealers in the twopenny trash, that what I intend to rehearse would have been set forth before. But it is well known that publishers have something more profitable to do than write books themselves. That trade is in the hands of authors, the operatives of literature. Indeed, had it not been for my ability to retire at a green old age, to my lodge of Linn, hard by the pleasant village of Deny, I would never have inked my fingers. The want, however, of other righteous pastimes constrains me to take the pen – not as an author that makes his living by his works but just in the way that idle gentlemen at a loss for employment, address themselves to tool-chests and turning machinery – in short, an amateur.

This much in the way of prelude seemed to be necessary, for I would think but little of my best friend if I heard of him writing for publication. Books may be as good in enticing pence into a till as any other toy but I never heard of a man making a fortune of rocking-horses or any other playock.

No doubt when I had my shop in the Row, it behoved me in selling books to put on – in the way of business – a very eruditical face, especially when I had new works to dispose of, but latterly however being in the publishing line and having more to do with authors than customers, I grew less sensible of the necessity of talking of genius or learning and all that, for I saw indeed that a man must have a two-fold nature to be a publisher. He must have the trade face, which is acquired in his apprenticeship as a seller of publications, and likewise that look of indifferency, which comes in years of discretion, and is as needful in buying manuscripts. But this will be seen more distinctly as I proceed. So having now explained the nature and object of this undertaking, I will enter upon the pith and marrow of it without further preface.

2

I am a native of Scotland, of what part there is no moral obligation to recite; but my mother was a widow woman, sister to the minister of the parish, who was a far-seeing man both anent the affairs of this world and the concerns of the two others that more immediately related to his vocation.

My father having died young I was left an only child, a cess upon my surviving parent, who was in a straitened circumstance and to whom – as she often said herself – if the minister with his good stipend had not proved himself a kind brother, she might have been a calamity to providence on the Kirk Session. With the reverend Doctor's christian help, however, she was enabled to warsle with poverty till I was in a way to put an end to the strife, the which began to kithe when he got me bound 'prentice to Mr Lorie, the bookseller that keepit the shop fornent the Trone in the Borough of Dozent.

I was then a well-doing callant, and when I look back on the innocent days of my youth and think of the knowledge I have since gotten of good and evil – by partaking of the world's forbidden fruit – I never could have fancied that I was ordained to fine for shirrif in the city of London, far less to bring out myself books in numbers besides works of genius that, as the critics I found it conducive to my interest to conciliate used to say, augmented the renown of England.

Being 'prentice with Mr Lorie I had time to improve my mind and to watch with gleg eyes the various customers who came into our shop upon the Wednesdays, for that was the market day. It was not that I had to watch them, though they were all of a literary turn, for being only readers of story books they were very honest country people.

It was not till I came to Edinburgh that I grew rightfully acquainted with the thieving of authors. They, to be sure, call it plagiarism – but that is only a slang term to denote 'poaching on the sly', as a divor gentleman used to say who I employed to superintend the printing of a volume of sermons for a clergyman that shall be nameless, to say nothing of a church dignitary.

Besides listening to the customers and running around and sweeping the shop and making up parcels and now and then taking a letter to the post office and shaking the can when there was a newing of ink and in putting up and taking down the shutters and in shining the windows when they wanted it and – in short – doing all the miscellaneous duties of apprenticeship, I made myself very praise-worthy for my painstaking; to such a degree that the master told my relation the Doctor that really I only needed to see the world to be in a condition to sell books with the best of the trade.

Well do I recollect when this conversation came to pass. It was on a Monday after my uncle had preached a great sermon the Sunday for the minister of the borough who was his neighbour and had made an exchange with him of pulpits for a day, both being in want of a ploy and troubled at home with a kittling in the throat which obligated them to try a change of air. My uncle, in the most natural way possible, coming into the shop and speaking about me and only of his great sermon as it were in a parethetical manner, said he had some thoughts of going intil Edinburgh in the spring to oversee the printing of a sermon before the General Assembly met, many of his friends having advised him to publish, as it might have the effect of turning sinners from the error of their way.

'Not, I myself,' said the sincere Doctor, 'think it will be so efficacious but it's in the Lord's power to make mustard seed into a great tree. But, as ye were saying, my nephew there, Robin Thrive, is a lad of parts. I have been thinking, Mr Lorie, that if he was not your apprentice, it would be for his advantage to get him into some creditable bookseller's shop in Edinburgh.'

'Never speak of me,' replied Mr Lorie, 'I'll never stand in the way of Robin's promotion for, although he's really clever and relieves me of the stress of business, I would not for something be an obstacle, especially if ye could get him creditably off your hands in an Edinburgh shop.'

This discussion gave me great insight of man, for it taught me the value of a good word, especially as I was instructed by my own certain knowledge that half of *my* time was spent in idleset with Mr Lorie. However, one thing led to another. My uncle in due time went into Edinburgh, printed his sermon there, and persuaded his publisher to make a place for me, his nephew, among his young men, representing me as a very superior boy to whom his master Mr Lorie considered it was doing great injustice to keep him in the occultation of a borough town – a bushel under a candle.

3

In the fullness of time when Dr Pockrify had made all clear for my going into Edinburgh, he invited me and my mother with Mr Lorie and the mistress to a tea-drinking at the Manse. It was really in a sense an occasion, for Mrs Pockrify his wife had two candles set in cut paper upon the table and there was a mysterious light and preparation about the Manse most miraculous. After tea we had a very sagacious discourse, the minister quoting Latin, and Mr Lorie showing his knowledge of the language by telling me aside that it was a beautiful passage from Demosthenes.

By and by we had a little bowl of hot toddy, for in those days tumblers had not come into fashion – 'deed, it was a better world before them than it has been since syne. In the making of the toddy the minister was very jocose, prophecying that I would be maybe in time a baillie with an outshot belly wearing my gold chain at the Cross, with my tail spread like a bubbly jock crousely strutting in the sunshine of a summer's day. But though in a sense his prophecy has come to pass, yet it was not in Edinburgh that I was ordained to be so triumphant.

When the cogie, as they called the bowl, was finished we had a garnished supper at which on one plate there were two eggs with a salt fat between them. The eggs were not boiled, for Mrs Pockrify told us that she never did such a thing till she got customers but she could recommend them because they were of her own laying. At the other end of the table there were chips of a mutton ham toasted before the fire and on the right hand side were four roasted potatoes of an oeconomical size and opposite to these two plum damas tarts that would have made the mouth of an older man than me water.

It would be too tedious to relate all the fancy things in the way of learning that Dr Pockrify said and Mr Lorie the bookseller expounded for the benefit of me and my mother. At last, the banquet being over, we all rose to come away, having finished a soop that was left on purpose in the bottom of the toddy bowl, Mr Lorie and the mistress being ready to go, the latter having put on her duffel coat – shawls not being then invented – the Doctor said to my mother: –

'Mrs Thrive, ye needna be in such a hurry. Besides on an occasion of sending your son into the world to a shop in Edinburgh, it behoves me by an obligation of relationship and calling to say to him a few words of edification. So sit you still and – as it's a fine night – Mr Lorie, having his gude wife to take care of him, will make the best of his way to the town.'

Thus it came to pass that after the great ploy that we had, me and the Doctor were left ourselves by the ladies leaving the room, the more effectual to make his exhortations. Accordingly, when the coast was clear, the Doctor began: –

'Robin Thrive,' said he, 'my lad, you are going into a sinful world, and if all tales be true there is a craft in the trade that you have chosen that requires to be weel cognos'ced. You know, my dear, that authors have long had reason to complain of a gall in their backs caused by their dealing with publishers, and I have had many sober thoughts on the subject, more especially as I cannot discern that if booksellers were well looked after they ought not to be worse than other men. I would therefore, my lad, advise you to think of this and, just in a canny way without a particularity, you can look after the sale of my sermon (which must be very great) and ye can just send me now and then a scrape of a pen saying how the sale comes on and whenever a new edition may be called for. It was really lucky for you that I put out my book in this conjuncture, because you know as I know well what number were printed. I can check Mr McGull's account, having your letters anent the sale.'

I thought that this at the time was very good counselling, but it went rather against the grain with me when I thought of the Doctor being so sordid about his sermon. In short, it awakened my instinct as to the inherent nature of authors, which is vera unsatisfactory and requires an art in the handling that (though I say it myself) I was not very diffident in learning, for in more senses than one I very soon saw the advantage of being a promising young man. However, to say no more on this matter, I gave a great relief to the Doctor's heart by telling him that I would not fail to keep in mind his judicious advice and to write him by James Dreigh the carrier every time that there were five hundred copies of his sermon disposed of.

OUR BOROUGH

BY THE DEAN OF GUILD

Chapter I

When we heard in our town the rumour of the Duke's resignation of the Government, we were greatly smitten with a consternation, for we had no doubt that it was an event that would be very soon followed by consequences, the nature of which was alarming to think of; for it was clear to the meanest capacity, from the signs of the times, that the Whigs would get the upper hand; and as they had been long currying favour with the Radicals, no man could conceal from himself, that they would, to serve their private ends, give them head-rope enough to work meikle mischief. It was not, however, thought expedient in our Council, that we should be overly forward in declaring what might be required of us to do, for although the majority were very firm government-men, there were among us some that had been considered for years as quisquous in their politics. Thus it came to pass, that the Tories, in a prudent spirit of humiliation, sat holding their tongues; and their opponents, fearful that the news were too good for them to be true, said nothing. So, that by our own free will, without having any communication on the subject with one another, we came, as it were, to a resolution to abstain from the borough business, till there was some certainty in our prospects, for surely it was a sore trial to honest men, who had all their lives upheld the King's Government, and who had often and often declared that they considered the din anent reform but as the routing of black cattle, to be put to a necessity either to abdicate their power, or to turn their coats.

But although we did abstain from the Council-chamber, there was a frequent and furthy intercourse by ordinar between us all; and a speaking concerning the monstrous crisis that had overtaken our national affairs. The Provost's Leddy held a great tea-drinking, at which we and our wives were all present; and the whole week there was a going and a coming among the bailies and councillors to one another's houses in the evening, that denoted trouble among us. I trow the toddy was not spared, and some of us stood greatly in the need of it, to keep up our spirits, for there is nothing in the life of man, in authority, so vexatious as to have a public charge, and know not what to do.

On the Sunday, the minister was in the poopit, a weighted-doun man, and delivered a most pleasant discourse, which had a great effect on all present, especially on Past-Provost Taigle, who was with the whole corporation that day in the magistrates' laft. Poor man! he was, indeed, heavy laden, and sat with his eyes shut, every now and then lifting his right hand and letting it fall in a serious conscientious manner. We were all greatly edified by the contrite way in which he kept time. It was clear to be seen that his foresight discerned something that had not kithed to the observation of men that were reputed to be of more understanding; but we remembered the words of Scripture concerning babes and sucklings. In short, a man with half an eye might have guessed from what he saw, that we had a terror upon us, as if the latter days were about to come to pass.

At last the post came in on the Monday, and all our fears were, without being ended, put to quiet. The Duke and the whole tot of his party were out; his Grace, and every respectable man of them were, it is said, seen coming out at a back door of the palace, with their napkins at their face, a sight most piteous. Sir Robert Peel was the only one who had not a napkin, but he had a green fan, through the spokes of which his watery eye was seen glinting like a blob of dew on a cabbage blade in a May morning.

As they were coming out at the back door, the Whigs were seen going in at the front. They walked seemingly with a sober demeanour, but it was all sham; they were there who saw them poking one another on the sides with their fingers in jocundity, for their hearts were full of ecstasy; and the Lord Chancellor was said to be snuffing the north-east wind, and pretending not to discern the Lord Advocate, and yet he gave him a funny kick, just as much as to say, 'Hurrah for the Blue and Yellow, we're the boys!'

But what happened in London in those days I shall not attempt to describe, for the newspapers have been most particular about it – my task is only to record what came to pass among ourselves, and how we were constrained to enact the part we did, and may still be obliged to do – until the Whigs are long enough in office to comport themselves as right officials, who, whether they are of the Whig or the Tory seed, soon grow alike. Indeed, the persuasion that sooner or later this must come to pass, is one of our greatest comforts under the present calamity, which rash, witless, and inconsiderate spirits call Reform.

When it was quite clearly ascertained that the rightful government of the Tories was clean broken down, and their adversaries seated in the power and glory of their places, we, as it were of a natural accord, held a meeting of the Provost, Bailies, and Town-Council, in the clerk's chamber, to consider what part we should then play in the tragedy that was under rehearsal. It happened to be a wet and blustering night, but we nevertheless had a full meeting, and a solid and serious crack anent the signs of the times.

Past-Provost Taigle, with his usual prudent diffidence, was of opinion that we ought to wait a little before we took any step, but Bailie Thummut was most contrary, and said, striking the table with his neive, 'that we would be disgraced to the end of the world, if we did not stand by our creed.'

'Have not we,' said the Bailie, 'been, since the memory of man, most true and loyal subjects, and shall we now make ourselves no better than apostates – for what? only because the Whigs, who have been little better than rebels and traitors from the beginning, have by a whisk usurped the seats of honour. We will not, gentlemen, for we have seen, not many years bygane, how when, with the soupleness of evil spirits, they slippit into power, that the grace of God was withheld from them, and being found nought in office, auld George III – he was a King! it will be lang till we see his like again – with the help of Lord Eldon, sent them a-packing with their tails atween their legs. Gentlemen, this uproar is but a fit – my advice, which I give with the help of natural sagacity, is to stand on our own feet, till we see how the rest of the nation incline, and then, if it be prudent, we can conform to the times, but if we shilly shally, or go over prematurely, we'll get no advantage.'

'To be sure,' replied the Town-treasurer, Mr Birl, 'what the Bailie has been saying is very much to the purpose; for if we go over at once to the side of the adversaries, and they are soon sent about their own business, we will be in a comical dilemma, neither the Duke, nor any of the Tories, who are the natural rulers of the kingdom, will put much faith in us again. I am waiting till we see the upshot of this anarchy and confusion; for, gentlemen and my Lord Provost, let us not mistake mere wet leather for a plaster. This is the beginning of a Revolution, and if we do not set a stout heart to a stye brae, the babe unborn may rue the day' –

'My Lord Provost,' cried Counsellor Capsize, starting from his seat, and interrupting Mr Birl, 'this is most obnoxious doctrine. If we wait till the nation have declared their conversion, where will be the merit of our coming in like wally-draigles at the end of the pick? No, my lord and gentlemen, depend upon't if we do so, but of small value will then be deemed our adherence. My voice is for an immediate declaration of our unalterable principles, and if it please Heaven to make a change back to the old condition of things, no doubt it's in the power of Providence to let us see what we should do, and to open our eyes to a clear discernment of our own interests, for I am not one of those who think that an honest man can have any other object in his politics than the promotion of his own interests, along with the interests of the borough or community whereof he is a member.' –

'Gentlemen, gentlemen,' cried Bailie Sterling, rising with a red face and an angry eye, 'can I credit my hearing? Surely we're by ourselves, to speak this open blasphemy. I'll no allow't, I will not allow't; we're here for the benefit of the public, and have no privilege to mint aught anent our 'dividual interests. We're here a part of his Majesty's Government, and have no right in any matters of government, to make our public trusts subservient to our private ends. Our task is to see that the laws are enforced; that's our duty as magistrates. My corruption, gentlemen, rises when I hear it said among us as magistrates, that we may turn our power to an advantage to ourselves. Gentlemen, it is rank sedition to say this, and therefore my opinion is, that we only see the laws executed. If we will mangle politics, let us do so as private persons; but it's not our duty as men in authority to do so. We have no authority to do so; I say we have no authority. What are we here, but seven men, and no wiser than our neighbours in a national sense? As men, we are free to talk nonsense, as becomes our natural infirmity; but all that we have been saying this night, is thrashing in the water, and a raising of bells' –

The worthy Bailie had not, however, proceeded farther, when Mr Sleekie rose, and waving his hand across the table to make him hold his tongue, said smoothly,

'My Lord Provost, this is no doubt a trying occasion, and the more it is so, the more it behoves us to ca' canny; but, without offence, I would say to my fervent friend there, that it's no consistent with a sound policy to expect that one is to rule seven of us.'

'My Lord Provost!' exclaimed Bailie Sterling – 'and am I to be domineered over by seven fools, merely because they think themselves seven golden candlesticks? They may be so, for aught I know, but where are their lights?'

'Really, Mr Sterling,' said the Provost, in his quiet, well-bred manner, 'ye must not speak in that way – I cannot allow you, because it's contrar to good order. – Mr Sleekie, you may proceed.'

'I have not much to say more,' was his sedate answer; 'but since there has grown up a heat in the blood of some of us, I would move that the sederunt be adjourned.'

'I second that move,' cried Mr Birl, the Treasurer, 'for it's very ripe and evident that we're no unanimous; but we may take up the debate in the morning; for, although it's not most convenient for us to leave our trades in the course of the day, this is a time of terror that may well call for an exception; and, therefore, I second the adjournment till eleven o'clock the morn.'

Thus it came to pass, from less to more, that we did adjourn till next day, for clear it was to be seen, that the element of strife was among us, and no good could come of lengthening our argol bargolling at night – so we skail'd.

It's a thing well known, that, from an ancient date, (if not before the Union,) it has, for a convenience, been the practice in our town to have a secret way of doing public business. This has commonly been by a hidden covenant between certain ruling members of the corporation, whereby, whenever there was a lawful council, that came to no conclusion in their differences, the aforesaid members went to some one or other of their houses, after an adjournment, and there, over a tumbler of toddy, talked rational on the affair, and determined how the thing wanted should be brought about. This was particularly the case when a new man was to be brought, by death or accident, into the Council, or when it was befitting to nominate the Provost or Bailies, or, in short, any other officer in the borough, whose qualifications required a previous consideration. This Privy Council, as it was called, consisted of the elect members of the corporation; and after the controversy in the Town Council just rehearsed, they adjourned to my house, to take the subject we had been pater nostring in the clerk's chamber into a more discreet handling.

It would be a needless defluxion of time, to relate what took place at the Privy Council we held that night, because the result will be seen in the proceedings of the Town Council, which took place next day. But the courteous reader cannot fail to see the straits that the nation was brought into, that we should be so obligated as to have three Councils in little more than twelve hours. One, a common nocturnal; another, a conclave in my house; and the third, a solemn legislature, held in the Town Hall, at the noon of day. Suffice it to say, for the present, that we continued our deliberations till it was far in the night; at last the toddy operated to its natural effect, and we separated ayont the twelve, with great cordiality. I well recollect, that Mr Sleekie, who was one of the Sanhedrim, gave me a very friendly squeeze of the hand, when he wished me good-night, and I could see that there was a tear in his eye as he did so, which was no doubt a token of his sincerity.

But no wonder that state secrets break out from the cabinet of kings, for even ours, and we were true honest men all, did not bide long in abeyance. In the morning my wife rose afore me, and she was not long a-foot, when I heard the voice of Mrs Birl in the passage, conversing with her about what would be necessary for a journey to London, and how she intended to go. But my wife, though very prudent in the main, was not to be trusted with the business of the commonwealth, and she was in consequence as much non-plushed, I could hear, by the questions of Mrs Birl, as if she had been an idol dumb,

Which blinded nations fear.

But no sooner had Mrs Birl departed the house than she came ben to me and said,

'What's this, gudeman? are ye going to London, and taking Mrs Birl and the Provost's leddy, and no me? This is not political justice, as I have heard you often say. Whatfor would ye be guilty of such iniquity?'

By this I needed no interpreter to tell me that either the Provost or Mr Birl had betrayed the secret that was not to be mentioned before it was confirmed by an act of sederunt in the Council Chamber; I however said nothing, but enquired, in a dry manner,

'What is the woman saying?'

'Oh, maybe you're no to be permitted to go yourself,' cried the mistress; 'and in that case I have no right to complain; but it's surely a terrible thing that the elect of the Council should be going in a deputation to see the King, and the Dean of Guild no permitted to go with them. I'll no believ't. So ye may as weel, gudeman, make a clean breast, and tell me all about it.'

Now I never could thole to be so questioned by the mistress in this pugnacious manner. So I told her to mind her householdry; but if she would gallant away to London, she could not ride a doucer gelding than her own spinning wheel. She was not, however, to be put off with a flea in her lug like this, but sat down in a chair by the bedside, for I was not yet up, and said, 'It does not look well for a married man to be shining away at London, leaving his rightful wife sitting like an ashypet crouching within the fender at home. And, gudeman! to be plain with you, if it's a reality that ye're going to London town, I'll go too, though I should be strapped on your shoulders like a packman's wallet.'

I had always a dread of my wife when I heard her so cool and condumacious, but I had some regard for my promise of secrecy, and so I said to her fleechingly, 'Dinna be overly outstropolous – by and bye, I may tell you something that will be news when ye hear't; but just let me be for the present, for I have a matter of mind to do before the Council meets this forenoon, that cannot be put off without an inconvenience. Go away, and let me think.'

Then she exclaimed, 'I could wager a plack to a bawbee, that this story of a cavalcading to see the King, with the Provost's leddy killyreeing in the van, is no without a solidity. A Council yestreen in the Tolbooth! A clishmaclavering to the dead o' night here! And another sprosing of the Council by day! Gudeman, dinna deny the fact to me – but I have my own fears. God's sake! I hope it's no in agitation to do any thing to the prejudice of our gude King, whom I have heard you speak of as if he were a nonsuch, better than Solomon?'

But although I was tried in this manner for a long time, I was dure in my determination not to speak of what might come to pass; so I got up, and dressing myself in good order, was in time for the Council.

The Provost having taken the chair, and the rest of us being seated round the table, he rose, and with a composed countenance, spoke to the following effect:-

'Gentlemen, after giving the best consideration in my power to what passed among us last night, and seeing that we are placed in a very difficult predicament as to our loyalty and principles, I have thought, and would now submit, gentlemen, to you, that we have no choice, in this momentary state of affairs, but to send, under the name of a deputation, certain wise and judicious men to London.'

'And what are they to do there?' cried Mr Sterling, who was not of the Privy Council.

'Their business will be to congratulate the King's Majesty on his accession to the throne.'

'That ought to have been thought of sooner,' replied Mr Sterling. 'But' –

'No doubt,' said the Provost; 'we had, however, no apprehension that we were in such peril; and in seeing the King they will have their ears open, and will hear something of what's going on. By the word they will send us, we shall know how to regulate oursells, for really, gentlemen, we live in an unco time, and what's to come to pass, no man can tell.'

'And who have you thought of, my Lord Provost, to send on this important business?' said Mr Sleekie, looking round to me with a pawkie curl in the corner of the eye.

'Upon that head,' replied the Provost, 'it would ill become me in this chair to dictate; but surely Past-Provost Taigle will not refuse to be one of the deputation?'

It was not intended he should, but it was thought, that for policy, he should have the offer, it being well known to us all, that as he was not a man of legerity, he would not accept it. It happened, however, that his wife's brother had come home with a fortune from India, and that the offer to be sent to London free of expense, was a fine thing for him and his wife; and accordingly he rose and said,

'My good Lord Provost – greatly am I indebted for the good opinion that my fellow-townsmen entertain of me, and of my small talents."

'No more than they deserve,' said I.

'And, if there is any way in which I can be useful to the community' –

'Hear, hear!' cried every member of the Privy Council.

'You may command my good will and best endeavours, but' –

'No, no – no buts;' and great clamour.

'I was only going to add' –, he rejoined, 'but you must take the will for the deed – I will do my best.'

All present looked aghast, and were as silent as it was possible for astonished men to be; for no one present ever feared he would consent to go, so that the members of the Privy Council sat dumfoundered, and those who had a suspicion in their thoughts, were just wonderfully diverted to think of the accident; nor was the matter mended by Bailie Sterling getting up and assuring the meeting that they could not have chosen a more judicious representative. Some that were there fell back in consternation, to be so taken by a side-wind, unexpectedly. However, the case was in good hands, for the Provost nodded over the table to me, which was as much as to say, 'Well, let this mishap pass for the present.'

But the perplexity did not end here, for Bailie Sterling, a quick, true-hearted man, stood well in the good-will of us all, as a conscientious man, though nobody, a minute before, would have thought him fit to be put on such a delicate situation. However, what he said about Past-Provost Taigle softened the auld man's heart and he, rising again, proposes that Mr Sterling should be another of the deputation. 'I cou'd-na,' said he, 'make choice of a man more to my own heart for a colleague; and since you have made me your first choice, do me the favour to appoint likewise my excellent friend.' And appointed he was.

An the Privy Councillors looked abashed – the whole plot was overturned, and what was to be done?

Luckily, as I have said, the Provost in the chair was not a man to be easily disconcerted. An adjournment was the only expedient that could save us. But how was that to be brought about? In a less cunning hand we were ruined, but having him, we were in the end triumphant, for presently he complained that the air of the room was close, and bade a window be opened; then he said he was all-overish, and at last he began to strain and bock. 'It's the Cholera,' cried all, with one voice, and the room was soon cleared of those who were not in the secret, and we then adjourned into another chamber.

Chapter II

Having been thus disappointed in the ploy of a deputation to London, by the manoeuvre described, which was no doubt a machination, there was not a member of the corporation that did not feel himself, all the rest of the day, in a state of uncertainty and tribulation. Those of the enemy's camp not expecting such a result, were afraid, not knowing what to make of it, that some hidden danger was in their triumph; and for our side, we saw that the whole affair was just a' nonsense, and would not be productive of any good, there being neither common sagacity nor a right understanding among those who made themselves cock-sure of the jaunt. But towards the afternoon we grew more composed, for the Provost, a regardful man, sent round one of the town-officers to tell us that we would be glad to hear it was not the Cholera which made him so dangerous. 'In short,' said Sunday, as the town-officer was called by the weans, in sport, 'he has just had a touch of the molly-grubs, which the leddy has pacified with rhubarb and brandy, and he'll be weel enough at night.'

Those that had discernment among us, were at no loss how to construe this message; and I accordingly went by myself, about eight o'clock, to his house, for I was very much consoled to hear the Provost had but suffered from a false alarm, and would, in the end, be the better of his dose of physic.

Going at eight o'clock, I found Past-Bailie Drivel there before me, who, though an old man and sorely failed, was not without a name for corporation business. He had heard who had been named for the deputation, and in what manner, and was, like every body of common sense, demented that it should have been so.

'But thanks be and praise,' said he, 'when we spoke anent it, the sederunt has been no sederunt at all – no minutes have been written out – the Provost's calamity put a stop to the business, and he has only to plead – which he can well do – that he was not in a capacity to preside, and therefore the meeting must stand a *dies non*, as it is called in the Latin language, in which these words signify no meeting at all.'

'Really, Bailie,' said the Provost himself, as he sat in his easy-chair with his wife's shawl over his shoulders, a cod behind his back, and on his head a clean white cotton nightcap, 'Really, Bailie, ye have thought my very thought – for, as sure as death, I was in no condition to argol bargol with any body, and ought – so great was my all-overishness – to have dismissed the Council before we came to the vote, and now that I think on't, the whole affair passed as a matter of course, without coming to a vote at all – It was just a kind of a hear and say.'

'Na,' said Mr Drivel, 'if that's the case we're all safe yet. Ye must just insist on making a *dies non* – and if I were you, and you had my experience, I would have no meeting at all – but say that it was an unregularity altogether.'

'But if we make a new 'lection for the deputation, the Reformers may again come on our blind side, and play another souple trick.'

'Ah, Provost, ye must not let them – just there where ye sit, in all the parapharnauly of a patient at death's door – send word to the Town Treasurer, that although Providence has been pleased to take you from your duty at this time, yet it has left you your head, and therefore as the business to London cannot wait, ye will dispatch the Dean of Guild forthwith on your own responsibility – ordering him to be supplied with money. And what's to hinder you, Mr Dean of Guild,' said he, turning to me, 'when ye're in London, to write down to us that ye cannot do without help, and then we'll send up to you those we know will be agreeable? Odd's sake, Provost, it was a very convenient stroke of policy to fall sick of such an outstrapolous malady as the cholera, so nicely in the nick of time.' – And Bailie Drivel rubbed his hands with fainness.

Just as we were thus soberly discoursing, another of the Council came in. He was one that we were not quite sure of, for on more than one occasion we had seen in him a leaning to the Radical side – and we could not divine what had brought him, for the Provost, as he afterwards told me himself, had most particularly directed Sunday to call only on our own friends. But it turned out that Mrs Canny, the councillor's wife, being vogie that her gudeman was in the way to be a bailie, always gave Sunday a dram when he came with a message on town business, and the pawkie bodie none doubting his reward, thought he could not do better than take the blithe tidings of the Provost's recovery to her door. Howsoever, the Provost fell into a low fit soon after Mr Canny came in, and as he could not carry on the discourse, particularly anent the town business, and the intruder was not on a familiarity with him, we soon got rid of that thorn in the flesh, and Past-Bailie Drivel with me, we stayed behind.

Presently the Provost brightened up, and bade us make another tumbler, and Mr Drivel, as he was brewing his, and brizzing the sugar with the mahogany bruizer, looked out over his tumbler from aneath his brows, and said to the Provost with a pyet's eyes, 'I have heard brandy commended as a medicine for the cholera.'

'So have I,' said the Provost, 'and if our friend the Dean of Guild doesna think it will do me harm, I dare say I could take a thimbleful.'

'Harm!' cried I; 'far be sic a thought from me – it's a medicine – and surely a medicine ought to do you good.'

Whereupon he drew his tumbler towards him, syne the gardivine, and made a cheerer that would have shamed to paleness the water of a tanhole.

'Eh! what am I about?' said he; 'but, Bailie, ye say that brandy's good for the cholera?'

'If ye hae't,' quoth the old man, again rubbing his hands, as if the palms had been kittly, drawing his under lip shavlingly over his upper, with a keckling kind of a laugh, that was funnier to thole than an advocate's pun.

Being thus restored to our ease and composure, though we did count on some others of our party coming in, we had a solid crack anent the signs of the times, for the London paper of that evening seemed to speak very ominously; no longer giving us that heartening to stand out against the reform which behoved an organ of the Government to do.

'Aye,' said the Provost, 'that is a sign! things are come to a pretty pass now. We are really cast upon an awful time. The nation's in a boiling confusion. Scum, pease, and barley are all walloping through ither. It is full time that we were on our posts; when, Dean of Guild, will ye be in a condition to go? Our hearths and altars are at stake.'

'The ashes of our ancestors,' cried Bailie Drivel.

'All that's dear to us,' said I.

'Yes,' replied the Provost, with solemnity, 'all is at stake, and the man who will not make a stand in this monstrous crisis, is a very worthless person.'

'But in what way,' cried I, 'is the stand to be made? I am ready.'

'So am I,' said the Bailie.

'The Radicals are up! the Whigs are up! and the Tories are crying for the mountains to fall on them,' said the Provost.

In short, we all worked ourselves into a consternation, in so much, that before old Bailie Drivel was half done with his toddy, his heart filled full, and the tear rushed into his eye in a very pitiful manner. But still we had between hands some sober conversation, and agreed among ourselves, that before manifesting at that time any change, or shadow of change, in our councils, it behoved me to set off for London, and write the Provost what was the signs and aspects of the times in London. And, accordingly, after a very serious sederunt, we parted for the night, and I went home to my own house.

Chapter III

Mrs Gables, my wife, was a person of a particular temper; by some opaqueness of intellect, she never could discern at first the use or good of any thing whatever. I mind well on our wedding night, she made an objection to go to her bridal bed, because, as she said, she did not ken the use of it and that comicality has aye staid about her sinsyne; and has so worked upon me, that I really stand in awe of her, when I have anything extraordinary to mention, for fear she mak owre great an obstacle. Thus it came to pass, that as it was late, when I bade gude night to the Provost, I was in hopes she would have been gone to her bed before I got home, but I was disappointed, for there she was, sitting up for me, a thing by common, and which was a very great surprise. But it seems, that Mr Drivel being with us, his wife had called on mine, and had told her something of the deputation to London, which Mrs Gables was just out of the body to hear about.

'And so, gudeman,' says she to me, when I went into the room where she was sitting by the fireside, her feet on the fender, and the candle needing snuffing, 'what news is this? It's no my opinion, go to London who likes, that you ought to go, especially as they say, anarchy and confusion are riding upon a Revolution there. The Gude preserve us!

what would ye say if they put up a gullyteen? Na, gudeman, I'll ne'er give my consent for you to run into sic a jeopardy.'

I answered her as well as I could; and having long discerned that she was easiest managed when spoken to with a serious solemnity, as became the head of a house, I gathered my brows in a very awful manner, and added,

'No doubt, my dear, what ye say is well worth a consideration; and if this mission was matter that rested with me, ye may be sure I would have had a pleasure in hearing the advice of one so well able to give me the very best.'

'Nane of your fleechings, Robin; ye're just fou', and tavert, and that's what has put it into your head to gar you think ye can blaw wind in my lug. But, is it true that there is to be a grand procession of all the Town Council, in post chaises to London, to give the King an advice anent the Reform Bill? Poor man, he's no out of the need o't. Surely, you that's been a king's man all your days, will never change now?'

'No, no, my dear,' said I, 'we have more discretion. Ye see, the case is this – that constitution, of which our corporation has so long had hesp and staple, is thought to be in need of a reparation; but there is an unco difference between a reparation and a reform; and it behoves us to look weel to that point beforehand – no that we have any idea of going over to the Whigs in the business; but you know we must be very circumspect.'

'Megstie me, gudeman,' cried Mrs Gables, 'are ye speaking of ganging o'er to the Whigs? you that was such a desperate Tory. I'll no alloo't – I'll ne'er consent to that.'

'My dear, I never intimated any such intention.'

'Don't say so – don't I know you, Robin, better than you do yourself? and don't I see the intention lying like an ill-coloured sediment at the bottom of your heart? If a' the world should be a weather-cock, Robin, sooner than turn a Whig, I would rust into inveteracy as a Tory. It would be a brave gale that would turn me.'

'Mrs Gables, there is no need to be so vehement. If the public good calls for a change, that change must be made; and my dear, what know you about Whigs or Tories that you should speak so?'

'Oh, Robin! what's that ye're saying? Do I not ken that a Whig is no better – ay, no better than – a yeard tead – and a Tory, is not he a magisterial man?'

'Well, well, let us not quarrel about it; but at an early hour the morn, I must be looking for the Glasgow mail, for if there be a seat, I intend to go by it to London.'

'No possible! gudeman! but I will have an explanation.'

'By and bye; but considering what time I must be up, we ought to be in our bed – Come' –

'I'll no move from this seat till you have told me all about it.'

'Een's ye like, Meg Dorts, – sit you there, and for all the turn you have in hand, ye may do as well without a candle – so I'll take this one with me.'

'Ah, Robin, when wine is in wit wavers – A wee drap makes you as dure as a door-nail. But I'll say no more this night about your town's-jaunt to London; for although I'm no an inch wiser concerning it than when I first began to howk the truth out of you, I ken my part, and will submit.'

Whereupon, notwithstanding her condumacious speech, she came with me to bed; but no sooner was I in, and aneath the blankets, than I considered with myself that it was expedient to fall sound asleep; for she was speaking horrid nonsense, as women will do that talk politics; nevertheless, though I gave a great snore to make her understand my condition, it had no other effect on her than to turn her discourse on herself, instead of on me, which she did straightways, by saying on hearing me snore –

'Poor man! a wee drappie soon gets the upper hand of his weak capacity, but I must counsel him in the morning.'

And so it came to pass, for she waukent before me, and giving me a knudge in the ribs with her elbow said, 'if ye'er really intent on going with the Glasgow mail, it is time to rise. But, Robin Gables, I doubt this jaunt is going a gray gate, or running a ram-race.'

'My dear,' I replied, getting up at the same time, 'I thought aye ye had more public spirit, than to put yourself as an adversary to your gudeman in a work of this consequence – deed, Jenny, if there be not a stand made now, or a concession, for we must do the one or the other, it's all over wi' us.'

'But what are ye going to do with the King at London – I would like to ken that? Surely he's not in such straits yet, as to need the support of such windlestraes? though it is my sincere opinion, that if he puts faith in the Whigs, he'll soon be brought to a morsel.'

'My dawtie, but ye have a bad opinion of the Whigs.'

'Is't no natural, gudeman, considering what I have heard of them, and their doings?'

'And what hae you heard?'

'Heard! did not you tell me yourself, when you got into the Council, that Whigs were most abominable, without a right principle, and save among those of their own way of thinking, they were not to be trusted? Think ye that I can broo folk so perfidious and blackhearted?'

'Far be it from me to egg you to do so – but, Jenny, what makes you so complaisant to the Tories?'

'Ah, are not ye one, my dear gudeman? and is it no my duty, as a wedded wife, to love and obey you? Besides, are not the Tories of a genteeler degree – wha but them has heretofore been the magistrates of the land, getting their sons sent to Ingy as cadies?'

'True, but don't you expect the Whigs will do the same with their gets, when they have places to give?'

'No doubt, it's natural they should; but I would not lend them a helping hand – Keep them down when ye have them down. What will ye say if they get the mastery? For my part, I'd sooner flee to where never one kent me, than yield an inch to them, far less strengthen them with my aid.'

In some discourse to this effect we passed the time till breakfast was ready, which, as soon as I had swallowed, I went to the Provost to get his instructions, that I might be prepared by the time the Glasgow mail came up. And going to the Provost, I found him up and sitting in his polonasy dressing-gown at his scrutoire, with a writing before him, and a certain sum of money, Bank of Englands, several sovereigns, and a bunch of his own bank guinea-notes at his elbow.

'Come away, Mr Gables,' said he, 'Come away – we live in sore times, that do not allow us our natural rest. Being a thought feared that ye might oversleep yourself, and that we might not have time for a right confabble afore the mail came up, I was just putting down with the scrape of a pen a word or two that might be seasonable; but since ye're there, it would be a work of supererogation to continue it.'

Then he laid down his pen, and taking off his spectacles, and turning his chair round to face me, he continued –

'We have not time to waster; so I'll begin and be even-down with you. Ye'll make your best ettle to be in London as soon as possible; then ye'll call on the Member for our district, and ye'll hear what he says anent the Reform. As he was always a true Government man – indeed had he been otherwise, he ne'er had been there – ye'll discern by the leaning of his discourse how the wind blows; for if ye find him against the great measure, say nothing, but let me know, and I shall then instruct you by course of post. But if he's what they call a bit-by-bit, ye may be pretty sure it's all over with the Tories, and may thereupon open your mind freely; but if he's desperate and inclined to be a radical, I'll no say ye may meet with a puzzler, but the chief thing that you are to do is, to see how the land lies.'

I told the Provost that I would exert my very best sagacity, for we had a great stake.

'There is no doubt of that,' said he, 'yet by a prudent handling ye may do much. But now what I am going to say is a profound secret between ourselves.'

'You may depend, Provost, on my discretion.'

'Well, Mr Gables, supposing you are thrown into a perplexity with what the member says, ye must then in a canny way try to get the ear of the Duke' –

'The Duke! no possible!'

'It's true, though; and as faint heart never won fair leddy, just go to himself and tell him what ye have come from our borough for; and as it's no in his nature to give either a crooked or meandering answer, he'll let you know what he thinks – which, if it be what we all fear, then go to the lad Brougham, – they have made him a lord, set him up! – and let him know, that we, seeing the great advantage of Reform, are in hopes that there will be a way of bringing it about, no overly much to our particular detriment, for that although OUR BOROUGH is no just so populous as Glasgow and some other Scottish towns, it is yet a very creditable place, and would do much to serve a man of his great talons.'

'Ah, sir!' said I, 'ye're, Provost, a far-sighted man. I hope we're not in such desperation.'

'But if we are, the best defence is to be well prepared. Ye'll then step in cannily to Mr Hume, and have some politic discourse with him. I would not just neglect Mr Holmes, even though ye find matters in such jeopardy. But, above all things, be sure and see Mr Place the Clothier, and with his help and creeshy handling, ye'll see Lord Grey himself, though it should be in the dead hour of the night.'

Just as the Provost was thus summering and wintering to me, our serving lass, Meg, came panting like a pelloch to tell me that the coach was coming; whereupon the Provost made an end, and taking up the notes and gold, put them into my hands.

'These,' said he, 'is what will maybe do for the jaunt. The Bank of Englands and the sovereigns are for after ye have passed Carlisle; but the notes of our ain bank circulate that length, and ye have of them what will do for the first part of the road in the going, and the last part in the coming; and I can only say, for a parting word, the motto of our borough, "Ca' canny, wi' the Lord's help." '

Having then given my acknowledgment to him for the money, as if I had received it from Mr Birl, the treasurer, I posted home, where the goodwife had the portmanty at the door ready, and the coach having changed horses at the inn forenent, in the nick of time I reached it, and was off before Mrs Gables had time to give me a word of solidity, as she called it, though I saw by her eyes that she had much to say.

THE DEAN OF GUILD

Introduction

The age of tales about love or murder, like the age of chivalry, is gone – nor was I ever very good at inditing such lucubrations; but, in its stead, a new epoch is arising, to which the events of the passing day furnish topics – a kind of light writing, like caricature in drawing, with just so much of true portraiture as may render the outlines amusing, while the extravagance remains so obvious that to the soberest reader the fiction is not equivocal.

My first attempt in this line was in the Ayrshire Legatees; but I committed a mistake, which has prevented that work from being understood by a few. I there made use of the real names of the actual persons with whom I intended to be jocular, and the consequence has been that, while I only tried to describe caricatures as seen by others, I have been supposed to speak my own opinions. I shall not, however, fall into the same error again.

In the 'Dean of Guild' I have endeavoured to be more perspicuous; and, therefore, I hope the attempt will be better appreciated.

I try to see things as I conceive a Mr Wamle may have looked upon them, and to describe certain public men as they might appear to such a person; but I have disguised their titles, ludicrously I acknowledge, so that, if I have erred in the outline of the intended likenesses, pardon may be the more readily conceded.

I have no other excuse for the liberty taken than that the parties are public men; and from the days of Coriolanus, all public personages must submit to show their wounds, if not their weaknesses, to the populace.

The Dean of Guild;
or,
Mr Wamle's Journey to London

When the nation, with the Reform, of which it had long been visibly big, was put to bed, it was thought that I could not do better in the crying time than take my foot in my hand and go to London, the corporation paying the expense, as behoove it to do, I going for the good of the community, and especially for the benefit of those with whom I sat in council. Accordingly, well instructed anent what I was to sift, I went into Glasgow and took out my ticket, being mindit to go by the mail, though our gudewife, Mrs Wamle, thought it would be more fashionable to go by the steamer, from Leith. Thus it came to pass that in course of nature I was on the road, and this writing is a gospel account of all I did in my mission.

The travelling to London by the Glasgow mail-coach is not a very felicitous sederunt, for it is too tedious, and, with three other passengers, is a sore hampering of the legs, insomuch that, before a man is half way, it could well be dispensed with. Nevertheless, from Carlisle, where we met with divers other stages, and took on board fresh passengers, we had a jocose party, all delegates going Londonward, anent the Reform. Among others, there was a most civilized man, who was the shirra of a county, and though he was, no doubt, a judge, he had a slake of the Tory about him that I jealouse was not in a conformity with the spirit of these troublesome times. Being, however, a discreet man, I saw he would accomplish the turn he had in hand, though if it were like mine, he would in the course of the doing find it difficult, and no bairn's play.

Much most edifying discourse we had as we travelled along, and it was the opinion of us all that it behoved Parliament, and specially the House of Peers, to make a timeous concession; for although a great deal could not be said of the good the Reform would do, yet it was required by the people, who will sometimes have their own way, in spite of reason and common sense.

Observes of that kind were not lost on me, but nourished in my bosom. 'If,' quo' I to myself, 'four discreet gentlemen of us, from four different airts of the wind, are all going to London-town on one end's errand, that surely is a sign of something:' and I pondered of the significance that is in the first verse of the second Psalm: –

> Why rage the heathen, and vain things
> Why do the people mind?

That, said I, inwardly, is a Tory sentiment, and would deserve a reflection, being in Scripture; but the Whiggish reply to it is really a perplexity: –

> Kings of the earth do set themselves,
> And Princes are combined!

And it is, I could not but conclude, because kings and princes are combined, that the heathen rage, and the people mind vain things. 'Now,' quo' I to myself, in my meditation thereon, 'it is as plain as a pike-staff, that unless the kings of the earth and the princes thereof, refrain from combining, the heathen will continue to rage, and the people pursue vainities. Therefore, unless the royal combinations, or Holy Alliance, can be put down, there is no hope of the people relapsing into moderation:' and I had a deep thought within myself on this head, the out-coming of the which was, that the world is turning upside down, and no one can prognosticate the upshot.

At last we got to London, a wearied man was I; and after getting some sleep in the publick where the coach put up, I hired a hackney-chaise, and went to the house of my wife's cousin, in Nightingale-lane, Wapping, to confabble with him where I should stay, hoping he would have the discretion to press me to bide in his house. But, dear me! the Londoners have no sagacity in giving names to their things: Nightingale-lane was just a grumphie close, not a path of more pleasantness than the main street of the Goose-dubs, in Glasgow. And as for my wife's cousin, Mr Harrigals, he was not just a man of the civilized world, for in order to get quit of me, as I thought, he, in London-fashion, told me at once, considering my business, that I would need to look for lodgings at the west end of the town.

He was glad to get rid of me, I trow, for he went down with me himself, and got a boat, that took us both up to Westminster-bridge, a long way, for a shilling; and from Westminster-bridge he took me to a neighbouring close, they call Manchester-buildings, and there we got most comfortable dry lodgings with an old lady of the single gender.

When he saw me thus fairly off his hands, he insisted that I should go back with him, and take a chack of dinner, as I could not but be so forefoughten with my travel, as to be in no condition either to call that night on the Duke, or the Earl, or the Lord Chancellor, whom, he said, was above them all. I accordingly went back with him; and, when we had dined, we had some very sensible discourse, concerning the Cholery and the Reform, over our tumblers.

When the time came for us to part, he got a cab, as they call it, which is just a whisky with a comical head, and a wee one stuck to the side of it, like a lampet on a stone; but it was just extraordinary how the lad that sits in the wee one, needled and worm'd through among the carriages in the streets. I was in a terrification lest some of them would rive off the wheels; and it was not without a reason that I was so for just as we turned into Manchester-buildings, which has not a facile entrance, the cab whambled against a stone, and before I could say megsty, I was sprawling in a gutter, and the misleared driver wallowing aboon me.

Mrs Reckon, my landlady, was a very thoughtful woman, and never forgot number one; for as soon as I got intil the house, seeing me all dirt, she recommended a glass of brandy, as my clothes were dabbled in the damp mud; but having no brandy laid in, she said that she would get some of her own speedily; and accordingly, as I made no objection, out she went, and in she came with a mutchkin, and gave me a running-over glass, which settled my inside. Shortly after, she came again into my parlour, and inquired what I would be pleased to have for supper – a lobster or oysters. I said that I was not fond of either: 'then,' said she, 'I'll bring you a Yarmouth bloater or a salt herring; for I had staying with me Mr Jobbry, the member of Parliament, and he was just delighted with a red herring, or sometimes a salt one for his supper, when he came from a dry debate in the House of Commons.'

This was so obligatory in her, that although I really was in want of nothing, I could not refuse her civility, especially as I did not know what a Yarmouth bloater was, and so I told her to get what she thought best; but I trow she, or all was done, made her politesse salt enough, for the red herring that she brought on that occasion, calling it a beautiful Yarmouth bloater, was charged in my account at the Samaria-like price of a whole sixpence. In other respects, however, except her weekly bills, I had not a great because to complain.

Next morning, having dressed myself, I went to see Mr Scripterson, the solicitor that we employed to oppose the great Foot-kite Bridge Bill on behalf of our borough, to take his advice and to consult him as to the state of the Government; but when I went there, lo and behold! he was a red-hot Whig, and could see nothing but balsam and plaisters in the Reform Bill for all the sores of the nation. I was really confounded to hear a man of his repute so far by himself, but my natural sagacity soon saw that I had committed a mistake in going to him at all, for all his life he had been employed in opposing measures, and naturally was with the Whigs; but I said nothing to him, only was very thankful for his shrewd counselling.

No sooner, however, was I out of his house, than I went straight to the other solicitor that was for the Bill, and he being an experienced Tory, saw the whole affair in a most proper light.

'Give yourself no uneasiness, Mr Wamle,' said he, 'this frenzy for reform is but a fit; it will soon pass over, and the Duke, with Sir Robert, will, in less than a month, be reinstated in the plenitude of their power.'

'Then, Mr Prosper,' said I, 'if the news be true, ye woudna advise me to have any thing to say with either Lord Twilight or the Lord Chancellor.'

'Oh,' quo' he, 'that would be most absurd: why, Sir, if there be no other cause, they must resign from inexperience; the Whigs are not men of business; they will become confused, and out they must go. It is as well, however, to let the country see, for a little time, what they are made of, and then the party is gone for ever.'

'Really, Mr Prosper,' quo' I, 'your tidings are glad tidings, for a change in the government is not an easy matter to a borough-town; for even before I left ours, the black nebs were beginning to shoot out their horns, and there is no saying how crouse they may become, if they get the upper hand. But what's your opinion anent my waiting on the Duke, for don't you think that he'll take it very kind to hear that we are standing by him in his adversity; for the which, no doubt, he'll have a consideration when he comes again to his kingdom, which, from what you say, Mr Prosper, surely cannot be far off?'

'As to waiting on the Duke,' said he, 'I am not sure that this is just the right time; besides such sort of personages are not very accessible.'

'That,' replied I, 'is very true; for I have heard that civil gentlemen are in office very proud, and sit at their desks

– as idols dumb
That blinded nations fear,

and are not to be seen in a Christian time; but the Duke being a soldier-officer, will of necessity be more easily come at; for when I was a bailie I made an observe that ye could na make a mistake in going to a soldier-officer, if it was on business, by night or by day, specially if he was an experienced man: sometimes the ensign laddies were a thought fashious to deal with, and no overly pleased to be disturbed when at their ploys; therefore I am none daunted at the thought of giving the Duke a morning-call just to inquire his opinion of things in general.'

Some further conversation ensued, and I thought Mr Prosper a little overly in dissuading me from going to the Duke, which was a matter that I could not understand. However, seeing him very Torily in his own opinion, I thanked him most cordially and then came away, and went straight to the Union-hotel to see what my fellow-travellers, who were staying there, had done or were intending to do; but it was not my policy to let them know the important intelligence that I had gotton, but only to spy the nakedness of the land.

I found them together, and with them the surviving magistrate of a town in the west, all with long faces, and each of them with a separate newspaper, reading the hopes and the dooms of their different towns.

'Well, Mr Wamle,' said one of them, that had the wide double flaad of the *Times* newspaper in his hand, 'what knowledge have ye gotten concerning this stræmash? – is your borough a gone, Dick?'

'Dear sir,' replied I, 'very little is the satisfaction that I have gotten; for, really, the Londoners I have been conversing with, dinna appear to have a mouthful of sense better than our own hamert folk; some say one thing, and some say another thing, – but, to trust to them, would be for the blind to follow the blind.'

'That's very true,' said another of the squad; 'and I think it would not be an ill part of the reformation to flit one of the Houses of Parliament to a canny and quiet country town.'

'That would be a radical job,' cried the surviving magistrate. 'How d'ye think the nation could warsle through if the House of Commons was out of town.'

'For my part,' answered his friend, 'I never could understand what either the Government or the Houses of Parliament had to do in

London; – it surely would be far better if they had their wark and their clatter in a quieter place.'

'It is because London is the metropolis,' said I, 'and naturally the head of state.' But none of the gentlemen understood this, though the surviving magistrate thought it a very good reason.

'But,' replied another, 'a reformed Parliament will see to correct that, with other abuses.'

'It certainly would be good for trade,' said the gentleman who was for flitting the House of Commons, 'if the Government went about the country, followed by the Houses of Parliament, in their own carriages. Would ever, do ye think, the play-actors stroll from place to place, if they did not find it for their own advantage?'

'Oh, sir!' cried the surviving magistrate, 'would ye liken Government to a gang of players?'

'That's most revolutionary,' said another of the gentlemen.

'Oh, we don't know,' quo' I, 'what this Reform is to bring about.'

After some more judicious confabble of this sort concerning national affairs, I took my hat and came away.

At first, as it was a long time till dinner, I was at a loss what to do with myself; for my intent was to dine at an eating-house, in order that I might hear amang the guests what political opinions were rife; so, after a hesitation in the street, I recollected that the Provost had given me twa lines to a friend of his, one Mr Gaut, whom he said was a man that would give me most excellent advice. Accordingly, as I had the letter in my pocket-book, I went to deliver it, and found Mr Gaut at home.

He received me with great civility, and heard from me what I had come to London upon; and when I told him of the story of the deputation, I saw his eyes twinkle with heartfelt satisfaction; and then he inquired how I intended to proceed, which led me to tell him something of what had happened with the two solicitors; at the which he observed, in a concerned manner, that he doubted if either of them could be of much use to me; whereupon I remarked that my dependance was not great on them, for my own notion was to wait on the heads of the parties – such as the Duke, the Earl, and the Lord Chancellor.

On hearing this, I could see a change come over his countenance, and his eyes sparkled as he said that the affair could not be more wisely devised.

'But,' said I, 'Mr Gaut, what is your opinion as to which of them I should see?'

'Oh, see them all,' said he; 'you cannot do better.'

'That's true,' quo' I, 'in a sense; but who do you think I should first call upon?'

'By all means on the Duke.'

'That's my own opinion,' was my reply; at which he gave a kind of a keckle that I wasna just pleased with, and said to him a thought sedately –

'Mr Gaut, I am very serious.'

'So I see,' said he, with a decorum face.

'Well, do not make a fool of me, Mr Gaut.'

'That is not in my power,' said he, more conciliatory; and then I begged he would let me know when I would be likely to find his Grace at home.

'Oh,' said he, 'you cannot be much mistaken in that, for the Duke is an early riser.'

'So I thought,' said I; 'soldier-officers, as my experience has found, are very accessible. – About what hour, do you think now, may I find his Grace?'

'Probably before seven o'clock in the morning he may be in his dressing-gown.'

'Aye, Mr Gaut, that the way to win battles; it'll be lang to the day before ye'll find one of our ordinary lords ready for battle by seven o'clock in the morning. – And what is the way I should proceed?'

'Oh, just go to the gate, give a loud rap, and tell the servant who answers it who you are, where you have come from, and what is your business.'

'That's no a kittle task, Mr Gaut – I can easily do that; but do you think I should make a particularity in my appearance when I call?'

'Oh, not at all; there is not the slightest occasion for that.'

'And so you think, Mr Gaut, he'll no be angry with me?'

'Angry, Mr Wamle! the Duke is not a dog, that he should even bark at you. But, before we proceed farther, remember you are to come to me after you have seen his Grace.'

'I think there's no use to lose time; if it's no being overly instantaneous, I may as well go to him the morn's morning.'

' "If it were done," ' said Mr Gaut, ' "when it is done, then it were well that it were done quickly;" and therefore breakfast with me tomorrow, and tell me all that shall have then passed with him. One word, however, Mr Wamle – don't let it be known to a living soul that you intend to wait on the Duke; depend upon it, if you do, some will think it a very extraordinary thing; and it may have an effect on the funds, which are just now very nervous.'

'Oh, you may depend on that, Sir, but, indeed, for your sincerity and cordiality, I would not even have mentioned my intent to you; but your heartening has taken the wavers from me.'

So when we had fully deliberated on this very important step, I rose to come away; but when I told him of my intent to gain insight into the politics of the metropolis, by eating my dinner in an eating-house, he offered to go with me, which I was not just pleased to hear; for it would obligate me to pay for his dinner, as he was so very instructive. However, I was resolved, while I was in London, to put a stout heart to a stey brae, and so I said how happy I would be of his good company; but as it was still, he said, too early, he would walk out with me, and shew me some of the lions of the town. This was most condescending, and so we came out together; but somehow he forgot the lions, and I saw only one on the top of a house, near to King William, Charing Cross, which did not appear to me a great ferley; but we saw a house with the bones of a whale in it; and, that I might make no mistake, he went with me as far as the Duke's dwelling, which stands in a pillary place at the town-end.

Having done all this, we came down, through St James's Park, to Manchester Buildings, and saw very grand things by the way; and in a particular manner we saw that monument of extravagance that has been such a cause of the Reform, the new palace of Buckingham House, and likewise other edificial structures of a frush nature, being plated brick: but I made no remark, tho' grieved I was to see such a waste of public money on unfinished edifices that are now building. Howsomever, one thing gave me great pleasure, and that was the swans in the water in the Park, and divers ducks, with droll eyes that were just curiosities. Mr Gaut, seeing me so ecstatic about them, speiret if I had not a few moullins in the bottom of my pouch to feed the water-fowl with, which was surely very ignorant of him to think a man of my years would have moullins in my pouch – I have not had such a thing since I was at the school; there was, however, an old wife with a stand of biscuits and English parliament-cakes, as Mr Gaut called them, at the yett, and we bought a pennyworth of them, and went back and gave the swans (stately creatures!) a pick, which made Mr Gaut, in a jocularity, to speir if it did not go against my conscience so to minister, in such times, to the sinecurists of the Court.

We then walked on together when we had fed the swans, and went in search of, as I requested, a creditable house, where we might hear the news and get our dinner; but I soon saw that he was not on very familiar terms in the coffee-house that we went to, for nobody knew him, and as I was an entire stranger too, the whole of the gentlemen there stood in awe of us, and never spoke above their breaths, but only in whispers; so I got neither news nor satisfaction.

'A man would need to know something of his companions in London,' thought I, 'before he talks familiarity with them.' In short, that dinner, the whilk we had together, was just a kind of *dies non*, though there was in a sense some diet, as I remarked; at which Mr Gaut laughed like a demented man some time, and then said, the king's fool himself could not have made a better pun to pleasure his Majesty. Soon after, taking up his hat, he proposed we should 'desert the diet,' which surely was very funny.

When we left the coffee-house, he proposed we should go to the play-house together, as may be we might there get some glimpse of the popular feeling, which I was so much in quest of, and accordingly we went thither; and when we arrived at the door, he inquired what part I would like to go to; whereupon I proposed that we should take our seats in the pit, and we did so; but I cannot say I was altogether at my ease there, for the house was as crowded as a kirk on an occasion, and a terrification of pocket-pickers came upon me that was not confortable.

Before we came, the actoring had begun, and there they were rampaging on the stage, and wringing their hands in the most disconsolate manner; but whether they were enacting a tragedy or a farce, Mr Gaut could not tell me; he was, however, inclined to think it was a drama, and when I inquired why he thought so, 'because,' said he, 'of that grand Turk in it, and that other ill-shaven man.' But, whatever it was, I could make nothing of it, and really it was very fatiguing to sit it out; but, however, at long and length, all the ladies and gentlemen performers came out saulying on the stage, and the fiddlers struck up 'GOD SAVE THE KING;' and all the congregation rising, there was as melodious a noise as I have heard for some time, which was gladness to my ears, and I said –

'There's no revolution here, every body is so loyal.'

Then there arose a loud ramping of feet, and a clapping of hands, and a fearful crying from the upper regions for 'RULE BRITANNIA;' and when it was sung, as it was with a dreadful birr, I inquired of Mr Gaut if the people had any apprehension that they were to be made slaves, they were so very resolute in saying and singing how they would not.

His answer was a consolation – 'You have heard with your own ears, Mr Dean of Guild,' said he, 'how well they have relished "God save the King;" no doubt, if his Majesty be a sensible man, he must have great reliance on the loyalty of this night. What better proof would any man wish for, that there is to be no revolution, than such loyalty? And you may judge, by the bray of the galleries when "Rule Britannia" was singing, by what an enlightened people the Reform is supported?'

But we were interrupted in our discourse by the playhouse skailing, which revived my terror of the pocket-pickers, for that is the time when they are busiest at their vocation. So we hastened out into the open air, and the night being far spent, Mr Gaut put me into a hackney, and was very particular with the chaise-driver, saying to take me home by the shortest way, for I was a stranger from the country; then bidding me good night, and telling me to be sure, after I came from the Duke, to come to him in the morning, he walked away.

But surely the playhouse was a long distance from Manchester Buildings, for the ne'er-do-well driver was more than an hour on the road, and stopped by the way at a publick, and had a bottle of porter, inquiring if I would not have one likewise. At last, however, he brought me home, and charged me five shillings, which surely was extortionate. The character of such cattle is, however, well known; and I did not argol-bargol long with him, but paid the money, as the Corporation was to bear all. I could not away with the thought, however, how Mr Gaut was so indiscreet, with all his knowledge of London, as to say to the man that I was a stranger; it was as good as to tell him to wander me by the way; and, as I had observed once or twice that he gave a sort of inward laugh when I was most serious, a fear came over me, and I said with an ejaculation, 'What will become of me if this Mr Gaut is not a sound man, and all his egging of me to go to the Duke be but a sort of divilry?'

But this apprehension wore off before I went to bed; for, although it was very late, I told Mrs Reckon that I would like a hot tumbler, being scomfished with the play-house – which she was not long in getting ready, having the kettle, as she told me, always boiling at night.

The toddy soon set me on pleasant terms with my circumstances, and, by the time I was in bed, I had pretty well considered what I should say to the Duke next morning; for there did not appear so rational a way of coming to the marrow of the matter as by seeing himself, which, upon reflection, made me contrite that I had for a moment misdooted the soundness of the advice of Mr Gaut.

I had not that night a composed rest, for my head ran all through it on the Duke, and long too soon was I awake. I did not rise, however, till after six o'clock, and, not to be unseasonable, I did not leave the house till I had heard the town-clock in the neighbouring Abbey chap seven.

My walk up the Park to the Duke's yett was very sober: I pondered well of what I ought to say, and the more I pondered, I grew the more perplext. At last I came to the house, and being counselled anent the rapping, I gave a knock on the brazen gate, as if I had been ca'ing a nail in with a hammer; at the which a fat gasy flunky opened it.

'Does the Duke live here?' quo' I.

'What Duke?' said he, looking at me saucily, from top to toe.

'The great Duke,' was my dry answer.

'What's your wife's name,' said he.

'Ah, ah!' quo' I, 'ye want to ken mine? – but ye'll look two ways for Sunday before I'm explicit; – but is this the Duke of Pumpington's? I kent it was.'

'It is,' said the man, a little cowed from his audacity.

'Then, my man,' said I, 'ye'll just let him know that the Lord Dean o' Guild of a borough that he knows right well, has come all the way from Scotland to speak with him concerning an extraordinary come-to-pass.'

I would not have been just so peremptory, but I saw by the looks of the man that he needed a dauntoning. So when I said this, he took off his gold-laced hat, and called me 'my lord,' saying, 'I did not recollect your lordship; for when I was in Edinburgh, with the Earl of Clawback, at the king's visit, my Lord Dean of Guild was, I thought, a different sort of looking man.'

'Very well,' said I; 'but let the Duke ken that I'm at the door.'

After some fraca with another flunky, I was taken in by him, and shown into a room, where, as sure as death, there was the Duke himself, at that early hour, sitting on an elbow-chair, with his legs dangling over the arm of it, in a festoon-like manner, reading a pamphlet.

He rose up, and having requested me, with the height of discretion, to take a chair, said –

'I did not, my Lord Dungael, at first recollect your lordship's title; but I perceive you do not come often to town.'

How could the Duke know this? I told him, then, that this was my first jaunt of the kind.

Then he inquired, really just like a plain other man, on what particular business I had come – which caused me to reply without trepidation, that in our borough we were in great straits, not knowing how to comport ourselves in the hobble-show of the Reform, and would be glad of his advice.

'Why,' said he, 'that's soon given: do what you think's right.'

'Ay, my Lord Duke,' quo' I, 'what would your Grace advise, if we were to turn reformers.'

'If you are so inclined, you have no need of my advice.'

'But we're not yet so inclined, please your Grace; for until it is settled that the Whigs are to keep the power, we have resolved to make no change in our principles.'

'A prudent policy!' replied the Duke; and I thought I could discern a downward crook in the corners of his mouth, which was not to the purpose; but, before I had time to make an answer, he again said, – 'But your business, my Lord Dungael?'

Now, what I had to do was not a matter that could be settled by such short questions; and so I said, in answer, very sedately –

'We are not sure among ourselves what is to come out of the Reform; and being intent to keep a calm sough, we would rather follow your Grace, if we saw that it would be for our advantage; but if there was no hope of your restoration, it behoves us to consider about siding with the Earl.'

'It is impossible,' replied his Grace, 'that I can be otherwise than delighted to think that there are many like you in the country!'

'Then your Grace does not yet despair of being taken into the king's council? – because, if you be certain of that, we will be true to the back-bone.'

'I don't doubt it;' – and rising from his seat and pulling the bell, he inquired of the servant who answered it if the *Times* newspaper had come; which I saw was a signification to me to take my departal, and I did it with all manner of courtesy, walking straight to Mr Gaut's, to take my breakfast with him, as I had promised; but, in going along, I chewed the cud of my pasturing with the Duke, and really it was not pleasant fodder that I had been eating. It was not of a sort that I could say exactly in what it was not good; but it did not lie so well on my stomach, as I had some thoughts it would have done, had he condescended to let me crack a little longer in my free way.

He may no doubt be a good soldier-officer, and clever enough at sticking and shooting the French; but he's not just the thing to make his way among honest people used to the magesterials. In truth, I had a doubt then, as I have now, if the Duke is of a statesman-nature; for, surely, though it saves time to be so curt with idle talkers as he was with me, it is not the way to make converts to ask for the *Times* newspaper. However, I suppressed what I inwardly felt, and put on the mask of a blithe face, that Mr Gaut might not be able to see I had been in a sense mortified.

With this rumination in my mind, I arrived at Mr Gaut's door, and was shown into the room, where he was sitting waiting for me with the *Times* newspaper spread on his knee. Well pleased he was to take me by the hand, and the very first words he said were, 'Have you been with the Duke?'

'I have,' said I.

'No possible!' said he.

'I do not say,' quo' I, 'that it's possible, I only say it's true.'

'Well!' said he, 'miracles will never cease. What said you to the Duke, and what did the Duke say to you? Sit down and tell me all about it.'

I did so, and he made breakfast in the mean time, saying – 'You are thoughtful, what sort of man in the Duke?'

'A very genteel, wice-like, plain man, but a little pernickety; ye cannot misdoubt what he says.'

'Then you are satisfied?'

'With the man himself, but I cannot say that what he said to me was just what I expected; he's a thought, yon man, short in the temper.'

Whereupon, on hearing this, I saw Mr Gaut's countenance gladden; but I could not discern any cause, especially when he said that plain-dealing was the Duke's way, adding –

'He's a sharp man, and cuts short and clean.'

'He may be,' quo' I, 'but sharp swords should have sheaths on; no that I have any thing to object to – but he's not a cordial man.'

'Ah!' said Mr Gaut, 'he's a Tory, and in desperate circumstances; if you hope for civility you must go to the gentlemen on the other side of the question; but how did the Duke look?'

'Na,' quo' I, 'that was the most confounding thing about him; for I cannot say that the man had just the austere face of an ill-doer; but some how, there's a want of something about yon man, and if it's not sympathy, I am not Dean of Guild.'

'Then, I fear,' said Mr Gaut, 'you have come little speed.

'None whatever – he didna give me time; but, Mr Gaut, I have made an observe, and that is, when a man's fortune is sliddering from under him, there is aye a giddiness in his head; and, therefore, the Duke being upon his peremptors with the like of me who has something in my power, is a sure sign that he's no far from a downfall. In short, Mr Gaut, I see that it will not be worth my while to call again on yon pot-metal man, for his day's done.'

'You make,' said Mr Gaut, thoughtfully, 'rather an impressive remark; for it's an old saying, that a man's wits and his fortune always go together, up-hill and down-hill.'

'If that be true,' quo' I, 'Mr Gaut, depend upon it, the bright and shining light that he may have been is passing to his setting. A saft word and a pleased eye would have made me his friend, and if our borough turns an adversary, he may thank himsel.'

'Then you are very much dissatisfied, Mr Wamle?' said he.

'Oh, no, ye're in a mistake there,' quo' I, 'but when a man is dividing a nation with another power, it behoves him in my opinion to be both more cool and condescending. The right in this world needs right handling.'

'Ah! well,' said Mr Gaut, 'so the poor Duke is out of your books?'

'Not just yet,' said I; 'he'll do very well to take his instructions from another – but he's only an executive man. I have a doubt if he think there is any other way of guiding mankind than by driving them. He's a soldier, and soldiers all must be led; they can do no good unless there is one with a head, you understand, to lead them; and we want a man that knows truth, and speaks truth just like the Duke, but kens what the Duke doesna ken – that the truth's not to be spoken at all times. I don't mean that what is untrue is to be ever spoken; but there is a judicious suspension of integrity that should be practised even when the heart is fullest.'

'Really, Mr Wamble, you surprise me; – but having now done with the Duke, what do you intend next?'

'I have not to a perfection resolved whether to call on Earl Twilight or Lord Besom first; and, as I understand that their tailor, one Mr Pension, has a great deal to say with them, I mean to have something to say with him before I wait officially on either.'

'You are very right,' said Mr Gaut; 'and I beg you to let me know what you do, for I am much interested in the result of your enterprise.'

So, after some further talk of this kind, breakfasting among hands, as he was going out on business, I took my leave of him for the day; and coming along, I began to consider with myself the best way of making an acquaintance with Mr Pension. – 'That,' said I to myself, cannot be a hard matter; for, as he keeps a shop and sells clothes, I have only to go to his shop, and speak to him concerning some matter of garmenting, and so gradually slip myself into his confidence.'

Accordingly, I went straight to his shop, and seeing in it a very respectable looking man, I said –

'Mr Pension, would ye have the goodness to take the measure of me for a pair of gumaushins?'

'Gum – what?' said he.

'Gumaushins,' said I.

'I never heard of such a thing,' he replied; 'what is it?'

'Now,' thought I to myself, 'here is a pretty sample of a political economist, not to know what a pair of gumaushins is!' I then explained to him that they were spatterdashes, to keep off the sparks of the street: so out of this we had a jocose parlez vooing; and if yon man was Mr Pension, we were soon on the best of footings. Then I said to him, just as it were by-the-by, that I had come from Scotland on a political business that would obligate me to see some of the big wigs of the Government; but that, being a plain man, and never in London before, I did not well know how to set about it.

'Oh, nothing is more easy,' said he; 'who do you wish particularly to see?'

'I have been thinking,' quo' I, 'that had I twa canny words in a corner with my Lord Twilight, my turn would be soon done.'

'I should think' said he, 'that may be easily managed.'

'Indeed! how?'

'Why, you see, he is busy all day with Government work, and shaping out tasks for others, and in the evening, he must be in the House of Lords; therefore, if you want to see him, you must so manage as to catch him after the House of Lords breaks up; and, therefore, I would advise you to call on him just when you know he has returned home from a long debate, and be sure that you do not then give him much time to rest himself; because if, you do, he may either go to his bed or be fallen asleep in his arm-chair; – so study to catch him before he has time to compose himself.'

This seemed to me the counselling of a very shrewd man, and, although I resolved to do as he advised, I was yet at the same time minded to say nothing on the subject to him, but to go myself that afternoon to the House of Lords, just as if I had no other end's errand there, than to hear their argol-bargolling. So, having come to this resolution, I inquired my way to the House of Lords, where I thought if I waited till the sederunt broke up, and followed the noble Earl to his house, I would be the surer of catching him.

Upon this resolution I acted, and went at the hour of the House meeting to wait, and there I saw, very comical with a queer wig, the Lord Chancellor himself, sitting on a cod, on the sack of woo'; and I was confounded. Oh! but yon is a clever man – he looked from side to side in a manifest affliction, because of the corruption around him. I had no notion that the rottenness of the State was so kenspeckle before, but on the whole, I was very well entertained; though I thought the play-actors, that I had seen the night before, spoke more to the purpose, and with less humming and hawing, than some Lords, for whose sakes I conceal their names, not wishing in these troublesome times to make them stand worse in the eyes of the people than they already naturally do.

It was a most entertaining thing to hear what the Lords did and said on that occasion. One of them, that I could see was not a member, in a certain sense, of the Temperance Society, said such bitter things, in so vicious manner, that the Lord Chancellor grew very uneasy: had he been sitting on a heckle, instead of a sack of wool, he could not have been more on thorns, and his eyes might have kindled candles. He turned to the right, and he turned to the left, and was just in a restless ecstasy, like a blue-bottle fly with a pin in its doup.

At last that Lord, who was really, I must say, a most provocative man, being out of breath, sat down; and up stotted the Lord Chancellor – and, I trow, it was not to seek what he had to say. His words were as elshins, and his tongue like a sharp two-edged sword, with which he run the other lord through the marrow of the soul, and made him cry 'a barley;' but, upon the whole, I could not discern the national advantage of yon birr and bantering – or, of what repute it can be to a Statesman to get the wyte of being an ill-tongued tinkler. Really, yon flyting made me very sorrowful; for, if they have such a heart-hatred of one another, they should fight it out: it looks unco' like a sham. I'm sure, the clashing of cold iron, that was the fashion among our forbears, was much more to the purpose than the spitting of venom out of a foul mouth.

At first, I thought that something deadly would ensue; but I called to mind, a fracaw between two old women, who had a quarrel something about a hen – and what they said to one another, knocking their neeves in each other's face, and staring with wrath, as if their eyne were pistols, and would shoot – was so very like the outstrapulous conduct of yon twa aquafortis lords; and yet they never, though I thought their mutches in jeopardy, came to blows. Yon may be parliamenting, but it's a humiliation to human nature.

After they had made an end of their barking, there was some solid conversing among the other Lords, which was endurable to hear after such a tempest. I could not, however, help thinking, and it's a real truth, that I have heard as much gumption spoken in our clerk's chamber anent the calamities of the kingdom, as among yon feckless congregation. They did not fill me with any awful ideas, though they were seemingly in a great stress.

The sederunt lasted till a late hour; and a discreet man, that stood near me, shewed me Lord Twilight; for I inquired, in order that I might know him when I went to his house – but, dear me! I'm sure he was not just the kind of man that I expected, but a slender, genteel man, with a bald head – very clear in the sound of his voice, with a style of language that put me in mind of a new-light preacher on his trial. He didna appear to me, what a reformer ought to be – for a reformer should be a sturdy, stern earl, with knotted brows, and fit to bear the riving and rugging of anarchy and confusion: a little short, stumpy character, with a parrot's neb, and a mouth speaking great things, would be more suitable. Accordingly, I was a little off my eggs – 'He's ower genteel,' quo' I to myself, 'for a revolutionary character; but I'll can better speak of his qualifications when I have confabulated with him, as I mean to do this night.' So being then a little fatigued, I was just on the point of going away to get a bottle of porter – for listening to orators is dry work – but it seems, I'm sure I can't tell why, the debate ended, and the House broke up, which made me, instead of thinking of the drink, to run down stairs; and I was just in the nick of time, for when I got to the door I saw the Earl stepping into his carriage, which I ran after as fast as possible, and got intil the street where he lives, just as it stopped at his door. I stopped likewise, where I then was, till he got out and was in the house, and the coach had come away; then, leaving a judicious interval, the which I measured by going twice up and down the street, I took courage and went to the door, with the knocker of which I gave a most genteel flourish, as I had done in the morning on the Duke's yett – and presently it was opened by a lean man; for his master, as I thought, had not been long enough in the possession of the good things to fatten him into a debonair appearance.

Having explained to the lean kine before-mentioned what I wanted with the Earl, what I was, and where I had come from, with how I was forefoughten by waiting the whole afternoon on my own legs in the House of Lords, knowing that his lordship was ower throng to see me in the regular hours of business, I had made bold to come upon him in his leisure. The man, seeing that I was a wice-like person, showed me into a red room, something between a library and a parlour, with grey marble pillars in the middle of the floor, bearing up the roof like those that Samson pulled down on the heads of the Philistines; then bidding me wait, he said, that although the hour was late, and all the rest of the household had gone to bed, he would let his lordship know that I was waiting to speak with him. Accordingly, he went out of the room, and left me alone.

As it was to be expected, I, being by myself, looked around at the particularities of the apartment, which, I will say, was a very decent room; but it was not grand enough, I thought, for the prime minister of our realm; and yet, though it was not so well furnished as the Glasgow provost's dining-room, it was nearly as big; but the furniture was a thought more odd, which, I imagine, was owing to its being a room for seeing strangers in, and all red to hide their shame.

By-and-by the door was opened, and the servant showed in a long, genteel man, with a powdered bald head, and called him my lord: he was of an erect stature, but of a pale complexion, very well bred, rather stiff, like the laird of Riglands, but he was more courteous withal; and had a white waistcoat, and a blue coat with yellow buttons, which was not like any minister's I have ever seen, for they always wear black – but a king's minister and a minister of the gospel are two very different sorts of men.

With more decorum than I could have expected, he requested me to ease myself, in a very pleasant manner, whereupon I sat down intil one of the easy chairs; but I could observe, by the tail of my eye, that he did not sit down himself, but walked about the room for fear of making himself ower joke-fellow-like with me: no doubt this was well ordered in him; but I called to mind in what shape I had seen the Duke in the morning, with his legs dangling over the elbow of his chair, and how he rose up at my entrance, and put himself in a more Christian-like posture; but, of course, I said nothing – only I thought to myself that there was more method and less freedom in the manner of the Earl than the Duke; and yet, to tell God's truth, I was at a loss to say whilk I would have preferred; for, although the Earl was more prejinct, and, I will say, of a genteeler manner, the duke was, upon the whole, a character better practised in affabilities.

As it was far in the night, I made a short tale, telling him of what an unsettled state we were in, because of the coggliness of the government – that we were greatly fashed about it, and the more so by a sough that had come forth how we were to be reformed and put upon a new footing.

The Earl heard me to an end very patiently, I think more than the Duke would have done, and one by one made answer unto the heads of my discoure, concluding, anent the Reform, that something was wanted; for that at present our town-council returned the member whose actions had as much to do with the generality of the burgesses or freemen as it had with the magistrates themselves.

Really yon man spoke very sensibly, and I could not deny but what he said was very true; but answered him, saying, that the burgesses or freemen, or what he was pleased to call them, who chose the bailies into council, knew beforehand that they gave them the power to choose a delegate to meet those of the other bourghs, and, therefore, no ill could come of the practice.

'That is very true;' said my lord, 'but the custom is not uniform throughout the nation, and the times require that a national custom should be uniform.'

'Ay,' quo' I, 'the *Times* is a very good newspaper; but on this head it is said to be neither well-informed nor overly correct about our Scottish borough.'

'The *Times* newspaper!' said his lordship, with a reddening look of surprise – but, in a moment after, he checked himself; for he saw that it would never do to give his opinion of a journal to which his government was so much beholden; and I, seeing this, changed the discourse, and came to my errand by saying, – 'And so, my Lord, it is your opinion that we should have a Reform?' – whereupon he replied 'I think so.'

'But,' said I, 'will the Houses of Parliament, do you think, grant it?'

'Why,' said he, 'the Commons, you know, have declared for it.'

'Ay, ay, my Lord,' quoth I; 'but ye ken the old by-word says, that it is a foul bird that files its own nest;' whereupon he gave a well-bred smile – for I jealouse it is not the custom for men of his degree to laugh like common folks. Howsomever, I added – 'But, my Lord, is it your opinion that the ministry will stand, if ye cannot carry the Reform Bill?'

'What then?' said he.

'Nothing,' replied I; 'but we would like in our town-council to know in time, that we might suit ourselves for the change.'

He did not give me a direct answer, but said, 'That is a question that depends on the king's will and public opinion;' and then added, that he was very fatigued, and really the newspapers seemed to know as much about the matter as he did.

Not to be unreasonable, I rose from my seat; and, wishing him a very good night, I came away, but not till I had seen that he was well pleased with me, and gave another of those polite smiles whereof I have been speaking.

One good thing came of this crack, though it was not quite so satisfactory as it might have been, and that was a resolve to read the newspaper more attentively than I had done; for yon reddening look that he gave me, when I spoke of the *Times*, is not soon to be forgotten.

I then returned to my lodgings in Manchester Buildings, where my landlady, thinking that I would be disjasked with the lateness of the hour and my travail all day, had the kettle boiling for me, and a tumbler with a soup of brandy in it, covered with a saucer which held the sugar; saying, as she asked me if I would have any, that she had put the saucer above the glass, because liquor was liable to be poisoned with the flies. I thought this was a very good observe, and when I had drank my toddy I went to bed, and had as confortable a sleep till the morning as I could have had, had my gudewife – as the old sang sings – been 'sound by me.'

This was on a Friday; and, next morning and all day, I suffered a great constipation of the understanding; for those who had come with me on the same end's errand were not to be met with – they were hither and yon; and it was plain to be seen that something was brewing, but what it was could not be well understood. In short, I was in great perplexity, and, by the time I went for my dinner, I resolved to see my Lord Besom, and put to him a plump question; but, before seeing him, I thought it was expedient to learn what sort of man he was; so, after taking my dinner in a most confortable way, I thought that I could not spend the evening better than in this investigation.

When I had finished, I went to the house of Mr Gaut, and had a solid conversation with him concerning Lord Besom; but I did not find Mr Gaut willing to be very off-hand with me.

He said that no doubt he was – meaning the Lord Chancellor – a very clever, fearless man, but too much of a hempie for him.

'Well,' said I, 'if that's your opinion of him, I will maintain that it's no an ill similitude of the man; for I saw him last night sitting on the sack of wool in the House of Lords, and really he appeared to me a very camstrary carl: first and foremost he louped up, and because he had nothing to say that was to the purpose, he made a long speech. "Hooly! hooly!" cried I to mysel', "if you expect to carry your purpose, ye maun e'en make your mouth mimmer; we would na thole such a rampageous provost in our town-council, and the rest of the world are, I trow, as debonair. For a time, my man, it may do you credit to be like a vitriol bottle, but a bottle of wine is more to the purpose." In short, I was not overly pleased with him when I saw him sitting on the sack of wool, and coming to the bar like an old maid in a Scotch measure, sweeping along to meet the House of Commons – so I wist not what to do; but Mr Gaut advised me by all means to see himself, and to have a crack with him concerning things in general. However, not to summer and winter anent this head, I very cordially agreed with Mr Gaut, that I could do no less than wait upon Lord Besom, and that, as a public functionary, I had nothing to do with his capering character, but just to send in my name.

So, next day, being the Sabbath day, instead of going to the kirk, I thought it would be employing my time as well by going to see the Lord Chancellor; and, accordingly, it being a smur of wet, I hired a hackney and went to his house, where I told the flunkie that opened the door what I was come upon; and he requested me to alight, showing me into a room where there sat, biding for my lord, a number of ill-faured persons, all sitting as glum as folks at a draigie.

While I was waiting, I had my ruminations anent them that were there, thinking to myself that they were come of a radical seed: for, said I, Whigs are really creatures of another-like principle: for the most part, continued I in my inward thoughts, there is not a very great difference between Whigs and Tories, and only, I have thought, that by their dress you could tell the one from the other. A Tory, said I under my breath, a man may always tell from a Whig, by his clean primrose-coloured gloves, lank habit of body, and very fashionable clothing. The Whigs are not so particular, but they have, for the most part, blue coats and washen-buff cashemere waistcoats: some of them, however, have parrot-nebbed noses; but I am a thought jealous, that those with particular noses are not right Whigs, whatever their bearing and speechifications may be; for I have observed, in the course of my life, that the parrot-nebbed are proud-hearted. Howsomever the clanjamphrey that I met with at the Lord Chancellor's were not of that kind of hook-nosed patriots which might have been there but an unwashen crew, with white handkerchiefs tied a-jee, and smelling high of liquor that is not called cinnamon-waters, though, I'll ne'er deny it, it may be as good in a cold morning when the wind is easterly.

By-and-by a serving man came in, and named the different groups; at last it came to my turn to be called into my Lord's presence, and I found him walking, in a most majestical and ministerious manner, in the middle of the floor of the room; I examined him well, and found that he was not fat, like Jehoiachim, but a spare man, high in bone.

After a while, looking at me with his nostrils as well as his eyes, he said to me, –

'So, you are the Dean of Guild of your borough?' naming our town.

I considered my answer well before I gave it; than I said, 'Yes,' looking at him with a scrupulous eye.

'And what has brought you to London?' said his lordship; which made me answer, that I had come by the Glasgow mail coach. Whereupon he turned on his heel, and his eyes were as if they would have kindled candles; but he nevertheless replied sedately, that he thought every body now-a-days travelled by the steamers.

'That may be,' quo' I; 'I dinna misdoubt your lordship's word, when I say that the world has in it more fools than your lordship's most obedient humble servant.'

'Then you don't like steam?' quo' he.

'It was a better world,' quo I, 'when we travelled under one peril; but now we have both fire and water. Eh, preserve us! what an anarchy it would be if a steam ship should catch fire in a storm, at the dead hour of night!'

He made me no answer, but drawing his hand over his mouth, which he has a great trick of, he seemed very well pleased, which caused me to say, –

'Talking of anarchies, my Lord, what are the private sentiments of your lordship about this change, that they're talking anent, in the king's government?'

'Aye!' said he, standing stock still, 'have they got that length? I had heard that they were very obstreperous about Glasgow, and that in Renfrewshire they were no better; but I never heard such a thing minted. What sort of business is chiefly followed in your borough?'

'Deed,' quo' I, 'we are of a sederunt sect – chiefly shoemakers for the export line, and muslin weavers of a particular faculty.'

'Aye, aye,' said he, 'that accounts for it; men of sederunt professions are very apt to be troubled with vapours from empty stomachs.'

'They couldn't have a worse complaint,' said I; 'but I hope your lordship, for all your sittings in Westminster-hall, and on the sacks of wool in the House of Lords, has still been preserved from vapouring.'

From less to more we had a very couthy crack, and he told me that wheat grew on cornstalks in England; and, no doubt, there would be an alteration in the Corn Laws sooner or later. I thanked him for giving me such important information.

Upon the whole there is certainly something in yon man; but I agree with Mr Gaut, that he would be none the worse if he rampauged less; and I hope it's no treason in me to say, if he would make his speeches less for out of the doors than he does; for when I heard him flyting in the House of Lords, it was less about the peers present than about some ones that get up the back stairs.

However, when I came to reflect at home in my lodgings concerning what had passed between us, I could not righly understand the drift of all he had said to me, yet he spoke a great deal; and when he was speaking, every word was as clear as a silver bell; but when I came to sift them in a composed manner, they were all timber-tuned and cracked, not a mouthful of common sense, buck nor stie, could I make of them; only I brought away a very distinct image of the man in my recollection; and I could na devaul from thinking that he might be a very good kind of a man; but the overly rouse of himself was too perspicuous, which I was sorry to notice for the sake of our auld country, Scotland, where we are a sober, sedate people, and never make our plack a bawbee, unless we see a reason for it. He may see a reason, I'll no deny that, for yon kicking and flinging; and I fain hope he does – I would be loath to think that it comes of natural carnality, seeing that is is said he was bred and brought up in the gude town of Edinburgh, the which, particularly the New Town, is for all manner of excellence called by the inhabitants thereof the Queen of the North, and the Modern Athens, with other fool names, however, that would take a Blue and Yellow to understand.

Thus having had, as they call it, an audience with the then stoups of the kingdom, I went home, and, as behoved me, I had by myself a very solid reflection, the orthodox out-coming of which was, that I could do nothing by staying in London; for really, as I could not hide the truth from myself, our borough had not a right influence upon the yeas or nays of the Reform; so I packit up my ends and my awls, and settling with that decent woman, Mrs Reckon, I put myself in a hackney, and came away that night by the Glasgow mail-coach from yon scene of corruption.

THE HOWDIE; AN AUTOBIOGRAPHY

Part I – Anent Births

When my gudeman departed this life, he left me with a heavy handful of seven childer, the youngest but a baby at the breast, and the elder a lassie scant of eight years old. With such a small family what could a lanely widow woman do? Greatly was I grieved, not only for the loss of our bread-winner, but the quenching of that cheerful light which was my solace and comfort in straitened circumstances, and in the many cold and dark hours which the needs of our necessitous condition obliged us to endure.

James Blithe was my first and only Jo; and but for that armed man, Poverty, who sat ever demanding at our hearth, there never was a brittle minute in the course of our wedded life. It was my pleasure to gladden him at home, when out-of-door vexations ruffled his temper; which seldom came to pass, for he was an honest young man, and pleasant among those with whom his lot was cast. I have often, since his death, thought, in calling him to mind, that it was by his natural sweet nature that the Lord was pleased, when He took him to Himself, to awaken the sympathy of others for me and the bairns, in our utmost distress.

He was the head gairdner to the Laird of Rigs, as his father had been before him; and the family had him in great respect. Besides many a present of useful things which they gave to us, when we were married, they came to our wedding; a compliment that James often said was like the smell of the sweet briar in a lown and dewy evening, a cherishment that seasoned happiness. It was not however till he was taken away that I experienced the extent of their kindness. The ladies of the family were most particular to me; the Laird himself, on the Sabbath after the burial, paid me a very edifying visit; and to the old Leddy Dowager, his mother, I owe the meal that has ever since been in the basin, by which I have been enabled to bring up my childer in the fear of the Lord.

The Leddy was really a managing motherly character; no grass grew beneath her feet when she had a turn to do, as was testified by my case: for when the minister's wife put it into her head that I might do well in the midwife-line, Mrs Forceps being then in her declining years, she lost no time in getting me made, in the language of the church and gospel, her helper and successor. A blessing it was at the time, and the whole parish has, with a constancy of purpose, continued to treat me far above my deserts; for I have ever been sure of a shortcoming in my best endeavours to give satisfaction. But it's not to speak of the difficulties that the hand of a considerate Providence has laid upon me with a sore weight for an earthly nature to bear, that I have sat down to indite this history book. I only intend hereby to show, how many strange things have come to pass in my douce way of life; and sure am I that in every calling, no matter however humble, peradventures will take place that ought to be recorded for the instruction, even of the wisest. Having said this, I will now proceed with my story.

All the har'st before the year of dearth, Mrs Forceps, my predecessor, had been in an ailing condition; insomuch that, on the Halloween, she was laid up, and never after was taken out of her bed a living woman. Thus it came to pass that, before the turn of the year, the midwifery business of our countryside came into my hands in the natural way.

I cannot tell how it happened that there was little to do in the way of trade all that winter; but it began to grow into a fashion that the genteeler order of ladies went into the towns to have there han'lings among the doctors. It was soon seen, however, that they had nothing to boast of by that manœuvre, for their gudemen thought the cost overcame the profit; and thus, although that was to a certainty a niggardly year, and great part of the next no better, it pleased the Lord, by the scanty upshot of the har'st before spoken of, that, whatever the ladies thought of the doctors, their husbands kept the warm side of frugality towards me and other poor women that had nothing to depend upon but the skill of their ten fingers.

Mrs Forceps being out of the way, I was called in; and my first case was with an elderly woman that was long thought by all her friends to be past bearing; but when she herself came to me, and rehearsed the state she was in, with a great sough for fear, instead of a bairn, it might turn out a tympathy, I called to her mind how Sarah the Patriarchess, the wife of Abraham, was more than forscore before Isaac was born:

which was to her great consolation; for she was a pious woman in the main, and could discern in that miracle of Scripture an admonition to her to be of good cheer.

From that night, poor Mrs Houselycat grew an altered woman; and her gudeman, Thomas Houselycat, was as caidgy a man as could be, at the prospect of having an Isaac in his old age; for neither he nor his wife had the least doubt that they were to be blest with a man-child. At last the fulness of time came; and Thomas having provided a jar of cinnamon brandy for the occasion, I was duly called in.

Well do I remember the night that worthy Thomas himself came for me, with a lantern or a bowit in his hand. It was pitch-dark; the winds rampaged among the trees, the sleet was just vicious, and every drop was as salt as pickle. He had his wife's shawl tied over his hat, by a great knot under the chin, and a pair of huggars drawn over his shoes, and above his knees; he was just a curiosity to see coming for me.

I went with him; and to be sure when I got to the house, there was a gathering; young and old were there, all speaking together; widows and grannies giving advice, and new-married wives sitting in the expectation of getting insight. Really it was a ploy; and no wonder that there was such a collection; for Mrs Houselycat was a woman well-stricken in years, and it could not be looked upon as any thing less than an inadvertency that she was ordained to be again a mother. I very well remember that her youngest daughter of the first clecking was there, a married woman, with a wean at her knee, I'se warrant a year-and-a-half old; it could both walk alone, and say many words almost as intelligible as the minister in the poopit, when it was a frosty morning; for the cold made him there shavelin-gabbit, and every word he said was just an oppression to his feckless tongue.

By and by the birth came to pass: but, och on! the long faces that were about me when it took place; for instead of a lad-bairn it proved a lassie; and to increase the universal dismay at this come-to-pass, it turned out that the bairn's cleading had, in a way out of the common, been prepared for a man child; which was the occasion of the innocent being, all the time of its nursing in appearance a very doubtful creature.

The foregoing case is the first that I could properly say was my own; for Mrs Forceps had a regular finger in the pie in all my heretofores. It was, however, good erls; for no sooner had I got Mrs Houselycat on her feet again, than I received a call from the head inns in the town, from a Captain's lady, that was overtaken there as the regiment was going through.

In this affair there was something that did not just please me in the conduct of Mrs Facings, as the gentlewoman was called; and I jaloused, by what I saw with the tail of my eye, that she was no better than a light woman. However, in the way of trade, it does not do to stand on trifles of that sort; for ours is a religious trade, as witness what is said in the Bible of the midwives of the Hebrews; and if it pleased Providence to ordain children to be, it is no less an ordained duty of the midwife to help them into the world. But I had not long been satisfied in my own mind that the mother was no better than she should be, when my kinder feelings were sorely tried, for she had a most extra-ordinar severe time o't; and I had but a weak hope that she would get through. However, with my help and the grace of God, she did get through: and I never saw, before nor since, so brave a baby as was that night born.

Scarcely was the birth over, when Mrs Facings fell into a weakly dwam that was very terrifying; and if the Captain was not her gude-man, he was as concerned about her, as any true gudeman could be, and much more so than some I could name, who have the best of characters.

It so happened that this Mrs Facings had been, as I have said, over-taken on the road, and had nothing prepared for a sore foot, although she well knew that she had no time to spare. This was very calamitous, and what was to be done required a consideration. I was for wrapping the baby in a blanket till the morning, when I had no misdoubt of gathering among the ladies of the town a sufficient change of needfu' baby clouts; but among other regimental clanjamphry that were around this left-to-hersel' damsel, was a Mrs Gooseskin, the drum-major's wife, a most devising character. When I told her of our straits and jeopardy, she said to give myself no uneasiness, for she had seen a very good substitute for child-linen, and would set about making it without delay.

What she proposed to do was beyond my comprehension; but she soon returned into the room with a box in her hand, filled with soft-teazed wool, which she set down on a chair at the bed-stock, and covering it with an apron, she pressed the wool under the apron into a hollow shape, like a goldfinch's nest, wherein she laid the infant, and covering it up with the apron, she put more wool over it, and made it as snug as a silk-worm in a cocoon, as it has been described to me. The sight of this novelty was, however, an affliction, for if she had intended to smother the bairn, she could not have taken a more effectual manner; and yet the baby lived and thrived, as I shall have occasion to rehearse.

Mrs Facings had a tedious recovery, and was not able to join him that in a sense was her gudeman, and the regiment, which was to me a great cause of affliction; for I thought that it might be said that her case was owing to my being a new hand, and not skilful enough. It thus came to pass that she, when able to stand the shake, was moved to private lodgings, where, for a season, she dwined and dwindled, and at last her life went clean out; but her orphan bairn was spared among us, and was a great means of causing a tenderness of heart to arise among the lasses, chiefly on account of its most thoughtless and ne'er-do-weel father, who never inquired after he left the town, concerning the puir thing; so that if there had not been a seed of charity bred by its orphan condition, nobody can tell what would have come of it. The saving hand of Providence was, however manifested. Old Miss Peggy Needle, who had all her life been out of the body about cats and dogs, grew just extraordinar to make a pet, in the place of them all, of the laddie Willie Facings; but, as I have said, I will by and by have to tell more about him; so on that account I will make an end of the second head of my discourse, and proceed to the next, which was one of a most piteous kind.

In our parish there lived a young lad, a sticket minister, not very alluring in his looks; indeed, to say the truth, he was by many, on account of them, thought to be no far short of a haverel; for he was lank and most uncomely, being in-kneed; but, for all that, the minister said he was a young man of great parts, and had not only a streak of geni, but a vast deal of inordinate erudition. He went commonly by the name of Dominie Quarto; and it came to pass, that he set his affections on a weel-faured lassie, the daughter of Mrs Stoups, who keepit the Thistle Inn. In this there was nothing wonderful, for she was a sweet maiden, and nobody ever saw her without wishing her well. But she could not abide the Dominie: and, indeed, it was no wonder, for he certainly was not a man to pleasure a woman's eye. Her affections were settled on a young lad called Jock Sym, a horse-couper, a blithe heartsome young man, of a genteel manner, and in great repute, therefore, among the gentlemen.

He won Mally Stoups' heart; they were married, and, in the fulness of time thereafter, her pains came on, and I was sent to ease her. She lay in a back room, that looked into their pleasant garden. Half up the lower casement of the window, there was a white muslin curtain, made out of one of her mother's old-fashioned tamboured aprons, drawn across from side to side, for the window had no shutters. It would be only to distress the reader to tell what she suffered. Long she struggled, and weak she grew; and a sough of her desperate case went up and down the town like the plague that walketh in darkness. Many came to enquire for her, both gentle and semple; and it was thought that the Dominie would have been in the crowd of callers: but he came not.

In the midst of her suffering, when I was going about my business in the room, with the afflicted lying-in woman, I happened to give a glint to the window, and startled I was, to see, like a ghost, looking over the white curtain, the melancholious visage of Dominie Quarto, with watery eyes glistening like two stars in the candle light.

I told one of the women who happened to be in the way, to go out to the sorrowful young man, and tell him not to look in at the window; whereupon she went out, and remonstrated with him for some time. While she was gone, sweet Mally Stoups and her unborn baby were carried away to Abraham's bosom. This was a most unfortunate thing; and I went out before the straighting-board could be gotten, with a heavy heart, on account of my poor family, that might suffer, if I was found guilty of being to blame.

I had not gone beyond the threshold of the back-door that led into the garden, when I discerned a dark figure between me and the westling scad of the setting moon. On going towards it, I was greatly surprised to find the weeping Dominie, who was keeping watch for the event there, and had just heard what had happened, by one of the women telling another.

This symptom of true love and tenderness made me forget my motherly anxieties, and I did all I could to console the poor lad; but he was not to be comforted, saying, 'It was a great trial when it was ordained that she should lie in the arms of Jock Sym, but it's far waur to think that the kirk-yard hole is to be her bed, and her bridegroom the worm.'

Poor forlorn creature! I had not a word to say. Indeed, he made my heart swell in my bosom; and I could never forget the way in which he grat over my hand, that he took between both of his, as a dear thing, that he was prone to fondle and mourn over.

But this cutting grief did not end that night; on Sabbath evening following, as the custom is in our parish, Mrs Sym was ordained to be interred; and there was a great gathering of freends and neighbours;

for both she and her gudeman were well thought of. Everybody expected the Dominie would be there, for his faithfulness was spoken of by all pitiful tongues; but he stayed away for pure grief; he hid himself from the daylight and the light of every human eye. In the gloaming, however, after, as the betherel went to ring the eight o'clock bell, he saw the Dominie standing with a downcast look, near the new grave, all which made baith a long and a sad story, for many a day among us: I doubt if it's forgotten yet. As for me, I never thought of it without a pang, but all trades have their troubles and the death of a young wife and her unborn baby, in her nineteenth year, is not one of the least that I have had to endure in mine.

But, although I met like many others in my outset both mortifications and difficulties, and what was worse than all, I could not say that I was triumphant in my endeavours; yet, like the Doctors, either good luck or experience made me gradually gather a repute for skill and discernment, insomuch that I became just wonderful for the request I was in. It is therefore needless for me to make a strive for the entertainment of the reader, by rehearsing all the han'lings that I had; but, as some of them were of a notable kind, I will pass over the generality and only make a Nota Bena here of those that were particular, as well as the births of the babies that afterwards came to be something in the world.

Between the death of Mally Stoups and the Whitsunday of that year, there was not much business in my line, not above two cases; but, on the day after, I had a doing, no less than of twins in a farmer's family, that was already overstocked with weans to a degree that was just a hardship; but, in that case, there was a testimony that Providence never sends mouths into the world without at the same time giving the wherewithal to fill them.

James Mashlam was a decent, douce, hard-working, careful man, and his wife was to all wives the very patron of frugality; but, with all their ettling, they could scarcely make the two ends of the year to meet. Owing to this, when it was heard in the parish that she had brought forth a Jacob and Esau, there was a great condolence; and the birth that ought to have caused both mirth and jocundity was not thought to be a gentle dispensation. But short-sighted is the wisdom of man and even of woman likewise; for, from that day, James Mashlam began to bud and prosper, and is now the toppingest man far or near; and his prosperity sprang out of what we all thought would be a narrowing of his straitened circumstances.

All the gentry of the country-side, when they heard the tydings, sent Mrs Mashlam many presents, and stocked her press with cleeding for her and the family. It happened, also, that, at this time, there was a great concourse of Englishers at the castle with my Lord; and one of them, a rattling young gentleman, proposed that they should raise a subscription for a race-purse; promising, that, if his horse won, he would give the purse for the behoof of the twins. Thus it came to pass, that a shower of gold one morning fell on James Mashlam, as he was holding the plough; for that English ramplor's horse, lo and behold! won the race, and he came over with all the company, with the purse in his hand full of golden guineas galloping upon James; and James and his wife sat cloking on this nest-egg, till they have hatched a fortune; for the harvest following, his eldest son was able to join the shearers, and from that day plenty, like a fat carlin, visited him daily. Year after year his childer that were of the male gender grew better and better helps: so that he enlarged his farm, and has since built the sclate house by the water side; that many a one, for its decent appearance, cannot but think it is surely the minister's manse.

From that time I too got a lift in the world; for it happened, that a grand lady, in the family way, came on a visit to the castle, and by some unaccountable accident she was prematurely brought to bed there. No doctor being at hand nearer than the burgh town, I was sent for and, before one could be brought, I had helped into the world the son and heir of an ancient family; for the which, I got ten golden guineas, a new gown that is still my best honesty, and a mutch that many a one came to see for it is made of a French lace. The lady insisted on me to wear it at the christening; which the Doctor was not overly pleased to hear tell of, thinking that I might in time clip the skirts of his practice.

For a long time after the deliverance of that lady I had a good deal to do in the cottars' houses; and lucky it was for me that I had got the guineas aforesaid, for the commonalty have not much to spare on an occasion; and I could not help thinking how wonderful are the ways of Providence, for the lady's gift enabled me to do my duty among the cottars with a lighter heart than I could have afforded to do had the benison been more stinted.

All the remainder of that year, the winter and the next spring, was without a remarkable: but just on the eve of summer, a very comical accident happened.

There was an old woman that come into the parish, nobody could tell how, and was called Lucky Nanse, who made her bread by distilling peppermint. Some said that now and then her house had the smell of whiskey; but how it came, whether from her still or the breath of her nostrils, was never made out to a moral certainty. This carlin had been in her day a by-ordinair woman, and was a soldier's widow forby.

At times she would tell stories of marvels she had seen in America, where she said there was a moose so big that a man could not lift its head. Once, when old Mr Izet, the precentor, to whom she was telling anent this beast, said it was not possible, she waxed very wroth, and knocking her neives together in his face, she told him that he was no gentleman to misdoubt her honour: Mr Izet, who had not much of the sweet milk of human kindness in his nature, was so provoked at this freedom, that he snapped his fingers as he turned to go away, and said she was not better than a ne'er-do-weel camp-randy. If she was oil before she was flame now, and dancing with her arms extended, she looted down, and, grasping a gowpin of earth in each hand, she scattered it with an air to the wind, and cried with a desperate voice, that she did not value his opinion at the worth of that dirt.

By this time the uproar had disturbed the clachan, and at every door the women were looking out to see what was the hobble-show; some with bairns in their arms and others with weans at their feet. Among the rest that happened to look out was Mrs Izet, who, on seeing the jeopardy that her gudeman was in, from that rabiator woman, ran to take him under her protection. But it was a rash action for Lucky Nanse stood with her hands on her henches and daured her to approach, threatening, with some soldier-like words, that if she came near she would close her day-lights.

Mrs Izet was terrified, and stood still.

Home with you, said Nanse, ye mud that ye are, to think yourself on a par with pipeclay, with other hetradox brags, that were just a sport to hear. In the meantime, the precentor was walking homeward, and called to his wife to come away, and leave that tempest and whirlwind with her own wrack and carry.

Lucky Nanse had, by this time, spent her ammunition, and, unable to find another word sufficiently vicious, she ran up to him and spat in his face.

Human nature could stand no more, and the precentor forgetting himself and his dignity in the parish, lifted his foot and gave her a kick, which caused her to fall on her back. There she lay sprawling and speechless, and made herself at last lie as like a corpse, as it was possible.

Every body thought that she was surely grievously hurt, though Mr Izet said his foot never touched her; and a hand-barrow was got to carry her home. All present were in great dismay, for they thought Mr Izet had committed a murder and would be hanged in course of law; but I may be spared from describing the dolorosity that was in our town that night.

Lucky Nanse being carried home on the barrow like a carcase, was put to bed; where, when she had lain some time, she opened a comical eye for a short space, and then to all intents and purposes seemed in the dead throes. It was just then that I, drawn into the house by the din of the straemash, looked over a neighbour's shoulder; but no sooner did the artful woman see my face than she gave a skirle of agony, and cried that her time was come, and the pains of a mother were upon her; at which to hear, all the other women gave a shout, as if a miracle was before them, for Nanse was, to all appearance, threescore; but she for a while so enacted her stratagem that we were in a terrification lest it should be true. At last she seemed quite exhausted, and I thought she was in the natural way, when in a jiffy she bounced up with a derisive gaffaw, and drove us all pell-mell out of the house. The like of such a ploy had never been heard of in our countryside. I was, however, very angry to be made such a fool of in my profession before all the people, especially as it turned out that the old woman was only capering in her cups.

Sometime after this exploit another come-to-pass happened that had a different effect on the nerves of us all. This fell out by a sailor's wife, a young woman that came to lie in from Sandy-port with her mother, a most creditable widow, that kept a huckstry shop for the sale of parliament cakes, candles, bone-combs, and prins, and earned a bawbee by the eydency of her spinning wheel.

Mrs Spritsail, as the young woman was called, had a boding in her breast that she could not overcome, and was a pitiable object of despondency, from no cause; but women in her state are often troubled by similar vapours. Hers, however, troubled everybody that came near her, and made her poor mother almost persuaded that she would not recover.

One night when she expected to be confined, I was called in: but such a night as that was! At the usual hour, the post woman, Martha Dauner, brought a letter to the old woman from Sandy-port, sealed with a black wafer; which, when Mrs Spritsail saw, she grew as pale as a clout, and gave a deep sigh. Alas! it was a sigh of prophecy; for the letter was to tell that her husband, John Spritsail, had tumbled overboard the night before, and was drowned.

For some time the young widow sat like an image, making no moan: it was very frightful to see her. By and by, her time came on, and although it could not be said that her suffering was by common, she fell back again into that effigy state, which made her more dreadful to see than if she had been a ghost in its winding sheet; and she never moved from the posture she put herself in till all was over, and the living creature was turned into a clod of church-yard clay.

This for a quiet calamity is the most distressing in my chronicle, for it came about with little ceremony. Nobody was present with us but only her sorrowful mother, on whose lap I laid the naked new-born babe. Soon after, the young widow departed to join her gudeman in paradise; but as it is a mournful tale, it would only be to hurt the reader's tender feelings to make a more particular account.

All my peradventures were not, however, of the same doleful kind; and there is one that I should mention, for it was the cause of meikle jocosity at the time and for no short season after.

There lived in the parish a very old woman, upwards of fourscore: she was as bent in her body as a cow's horn, and she supported herself with a staff in one hand, and for balance held up her gown behind with the other; in short, she was a very antideluvian, something older than seemed the folk at that time of the earth.

This ancient crone was the grandmother to Lizzy Dadily, a light-headed winsome lassie, that went to service in Glasgow; but many months she had not been there when she came back again, all mouth and een; and on the same night her granny, old Maudelin, called on me. It was at the gloaming: I had not trimmed my crusie, but I had just mended the fire, which had not broken out so that we conversed in an obscurity.

Of the history of old Maudelin I had never before heard ony particulars; but her father, as she told me, was out in the rebellion of Mar's year, and if the true king had gotten his rights, she would not have been a needful woman. This I, however, jealouse was vanity; for although it could not be said that she was positively an ill-doer, it was well known in the town that old as she was, the conduct of her house in many points was not the best. Her daughter, the mother of Lizzy, was but a canary-headed creature. What became of her we never heard, for she went off with the soldiers one day, leaving Lizzy, a bastard bairn. How the old woman thereafter fenn't, in her warsle with age and poverty, was to many a mystery, especially as it was now and then seen that she had a bank guinea note to change, and whom it cam frae was a marvel.

Lizzy coming home, her granny came to me, as I was saying, and after awhile conversing in the twilight about this and that, she told me that she was afraid her oe had brought home her wark, and that she didna doubt they would need the sleight of my hand in a short time, for that Lizzy had only got a month's leave to try the benefit of her native air; that of Glasgow, as with most young women, not agreeing with her.

I was greatly taken aback to her hear talk in such a calm and methodical manner concerning Lizzy, whom I soon found was in that condition that would, I'm sure, have drawn tears of the heart's blood from every other grandmother in the clachan. Really I was not well pleased to her the sinful carlin talk in such a good-e'en and good-morn way about a guilt of that nature; and I said to her, both hooly and fairly, that I was not sure if I could engage myself in the business, for it went against my righteous opinion to make myself a mean of filling the world with natural children.

The old woman was not just pleased to her me say this, and without any honey on her lips, she replied,

'Widow Blithe, this is an unco strain! and what for will ye no do your duty to Lizzy Dadily; for I must have a reason, because the minister or the magistrates of the borough shall ken of this.'

I was to be sure a little confounded to hear the frail though bardy old woman thus speak to her peremptors, but in my mild and methodical manner I answered and said,

'That no person in a trade with full hands ought to take a new turn; and although conscience, I would allow, had its weight with me, yet there was a stronger reason in my engagements to others.'

'Very well,' said Maudelin, and hastily rising, she gave a rap with her staff, and said, 'that there soon would be news in the land that I would hear of;' and away she went, stotting out at the door, notwithstanding her age, like a birsled pea.

After she was gone, I began to reflect; and I cannot say that I had just an ease of mind, when I thought of what she had been telling anent her oe: but nothing more came to pass that night.

The following evening, however, about the same hour, who should darken my door but the minister himself, a most discreet man, who had always paid me a very sympathysing attention from the death of my gudeman; so I received him with the greatest respect, wondering what could bring him to see me at that doubtful hour. But no sooner had he taken a seat in the elbow chair than he made my hair stand on end at the wickedness and perfidy of the woman sec.

'Mrs Blithe,' said he, 'I have come to have a serious word with you, and to talk with you on a subject that is impossible for me to believe. Last night that old Maudelin, of whom the world speaks no good, came to me with her grand-daughter from Glasgow, both weeping very bitterly; the poor young lass had her apron tail at her face, and was in great distress.'

'What is the matter with you,' said I, quoth the minister; 'and thereupon the piteous grandmother told me that her oe had been beguiled by a false manufacturing gentleman, and was thereby constrained to come back in a state of ignominy that was heartbreaking.'

'Good Maudelin, in what can I help you in your calamity?'

'In nothing, nothing,' said she; 'but we are come to make a confession in time.'

'What confession? quo' I' – that said the minister.

'Oh, sir,' said she, 'it's dreadful, but your counselling may rescue us from a great guilt. I have just been with Widow Blithe, the midwife, to bespeak her helping hand; oh, sir, speir no questions.'

'But,' said the minister, 'this is not a business to be trifled with; what did Mrs Blithe say to you?'

'That Mrs Blithe,' replied Maudelin, 'is a hidden woman; she made sport of my poor Lizzy's misfortune, and said that the best I could do was to let her nip the craig of the bairn in the hour of its birth.'

'Now, Mrs Blithe,' continued the Minister, 'is it possible that you could suggest such a crime?'

I was speechless; blue sterns danced before my sight, my knees trembled, and the steadfast earth grew as it were coggly aneath my chair; at last I replied,

'That old woman, sir, is of a nature, as she is of age enough, to be a witch – she's no canny! to even me to murder! Sir, I commit myself into your hands and judgment.'

'Indeed, I thought,' said the minister, 'that you would never speak as Maudelin said you had done; but she told me to examine you myself, for that she was sure, if I was put to the straights of a question, I would tell the truth.'

'And you have heard the truth, sir,' cried I.

'I believe it,' said he; 'but, in addition to all she rehearsed, she told me that, unless you, Mrs Blithe, would do your duty to her injured oe, and free gratis for no fee at all, she would go before a magistrate, and swear you had egged her on to bathe her hands in innocent infant blood.'

'Mr Stipend,' cried I; 'the wickedness of the human heart is beyond the computations of man: this dreadful old woman is, I'll not say what; but oh, sir, what am I to do; for if she makes a perjury to a magistrate my trade is gone, and my dear bairns driven to iniquity and beggary?'

Then the minister shook his head, and said, 'It was, to be sure, a great trial, for a worthy woman like me, to be so squeezed in the vice of malice and malignity; but a calm sough in all troubles was true wisdom, and that I ought to comply with the deceitful carlin's terms.'

Thus it came to pass, that, after the bastard brat was born, the old wife made a brag of how she had spirited the worthy minister to terrify me. Everybody laughed at her souple trick: but to me it was, for many a day, a heartburning; though, to the laive of the parish, it was a great mean, as I have said, of daffin and merriment.

No doubt, it will be seen, by the foregoing, that, although in a sense I had reason to be thankful that Providence, with the help of the laird's leddy-mother, had enabled me to make a bit of bread for my family, yet, it was not always without a trouble and an anxiety. Indeed, when I think on what I have come through in my profession, though it be one of the learned, and the world not able to do without it, I have often thought that I could not wish waur to my deadliest enemy than a kittle case of midwifery; for surely it is a very obstetrical business, and far above a woman with common talons to practise. But it would be to make a wearisome tale were I to lengthen my story; and so I mean just to tell of another accident that happened to me last year, and then to make an end, with a word or two of improvement on what shall have been said; afterwards I will give some account of what happened to those that, through my instrumentality, were brought to be a credit to themselves and an ornament to the world. Some, it is very true, were not just of that stamp; for, as the impartial sun shines alike on the wicked and the worthy, I have had to deal with those whose use I never could see, more than that of an apple that falleth from the tree, and perisheth with rottenness.

The case that I have to conclude with was in some sort mystical; and long it was before I got an interpretation thereof. It happened thus: –

One morning in the fall of the year and before break of day, when I was lying wakerife in my bed, I heard a knuckling on the pane of the window and got up to inquire the cause. This was by the porter of the Thistle Inns, seeking my help for a leddy at the crying, that had come to their house since midnight and could go no further.

I made no more ado, but dressed myself off-hand, and went to the Inns; where, to be sure, there was a leddy, for any thing that I then knew to the contrary, in great difficulty. Who she was, and where she had come from, I heard not; nor did I speir; nor did I see her face; for over her whole head she had a muslin apron so thrown and tied, that her face was concealed; and no persuasion could get her to remove that veil. It was therefore plain to me that she wished herself, even in my hands, not to be known; but she did not seem to jalouse that the very obstinacy about the veil would be a cause to make me think that she was afraid I would know her. I was not, however, overly-curious; for, among the other good advices that I got when I was about to take up the trade, from the leddy of Rigs, my patron, I was enjoined never to be inquisitive anent family secrets; which I have, with a very scrupulous care, always adhered to; and thus it happened, that, although the leddy made herself so strange as to make me suspicious that all was not right, I said nothing but I opened both my eyes and my ears.

She had with her an elderly woman; and, before she came to the worst, I could gather from their discourse, that the lady's husband was expected every day from some foreign land. By and by, what with putting one thing together with another, and eiking out with the help of my own imagination, I was fain to guess that she would not be ill pleased to be quit of her burden before the Major came home.

Nothing beyond this patch-work of hints then occurred. She had an easy time of it; and, before the sun was up, she was the mother of a bonny bairn. But what surprised me was, that, in less than an hour after the birth, she was so wonderful hale and hearty, that she spoke of travelling another stage in the course of the day, and of leaving Mrs Smith, that was with her, behind to take care of the babby; indeed, this was settled; and, before noon, at twelve o'clock, she was ready to step into the post-chaise that she had ordered to take herself forward – but mark the upshot.

When she was dressed and ready for the road – really she was a stout woman – another chaise drew up at the Inn's door, and, on looking from the window to see who was in it, she gave a shriek and staggered back to a sofa, upon which she fell like one that had been dumbfoundered.

In the chaise I saw only an elderly weather-beaten gentleman, who, as soon as the horses were changed, pursued his journey. The moment he was off, this mysterious mother called the lady-nurse with the babby, and they spoke for a time in whispers. Then her chaise was brought out and in she stepped, causing me to go with her for a stage. I did so and she very liberally gave me a five pound note of the Royal Bank and made me, without allowing me to alight, return back with the retour-chaise; for the which, on my account, she settled with the driver. But there the story did not rest, as I shall have occasion to rehearse by and by.

Part II – Anent Bairns

Although I have not in the foregoing head of my subject mentioned every extraordinary han'ling that came to me, yet I have noted the most remarkable; and made it plain to my readers by that swatch of my professional work, that it is not an easy thing to be a midwife with repute, without the inheritance from nature of good common sense and discretion, over and above skill and experience. I shall now dedicate this second head, to a make-mention of such things as I have heard and known anent the bairns, that in their entrance into this world, came by the grace of God through my hands.

And here, in the first place, and at the very outset, it behoves me to make an observe, that neither omen nor symptom occurs at a birth, by which any reasonable person or gossip present can foretell what the native, as the unchristened baby is then called, may be ordained to come through in the course of the future. No doubt this generality, like every rule, has an exception; but I am no disposed to think the exceptions often kent-speckle; for although I have heard many a well-doing sagacious carlin notice the remarkables she had seen at some births, I am yet bound to say that my experience has never taught me to discern in what way a-come-to-pass in the life of the man was begotten of the uncos at the birth of the child.

But while I say this, let me no be misunderstood as throwing any doubt on the fact, that births sometimes are, and have been, in all ages, attended with signs and wonders manifest. I am only stating the truth it has fallen out in the course of my own experience; for I never mis-doubt that it's in the power of Providence to work miracles and cause marvels, when a child is ordained with a superfluity of head-rope. I only maintain, that it is not a constancy in nature to be regular in that way, and that many prodigies happen at the times of births, of which it would not be a facile thing for a very wise prophet to expound the use. Indeed, my observes would go to the clean contrary; for I have noted that, for the most part, the births which have happened in dread and strange circumstances, were not a hair's-breadth better, than those of the commonest clamjamphry. Indeed, I had a very notable instance of this kind in the very first year of my setting up for myself, and that was when James Cuiffy's wife lay in of her eldest born.

James, as all the parish well knew, was not a man to lead the children of Israel through the Red Sea, nor she a Deborah to sing of butter in a lordly dish; but they were decent folk; and when the fulness of her time was come, it behoved her to be put to bed, and my helping hand to be called for. Accordingly I went.

It was the gloaming when James came for me; and as we walked o'er the craft together, the summer lightning ayont the hills began to skimmer in a woolly cloud: but we thought little o't, for the day had been very warm, and that flabbing of the fire was but a natural outcoming of the same cause.

We had not, however, been under the shelter of the roof many minutes, when we heard a-far off, like the ruff of a drum or the hurl of a cart of stones tumbled on the causey, a clap of thunder, and then we heard another and another, just like a sea-fight of Royal Georges in the skies, till the din grew so desperate, that the crying woman could no more be heard than if she had been a stone image of agony.

I'll no say that I was not in a terrification. James Cuiffy took to his Bible, but the poor wife needed all my help. At last the bairn was born; and just as it came into the world, the thunder rampaged, as if the Prince of the Powers of the air had gaen by himself; and in the same minute, a thunder-bolt fell doun the lum, scattered the fire about the house, whiskit out of the window, clove like a wedge the apple-tree at the house-end, and slew nine sucking pigs and the mother grumphy, as if they had been no better than the host of Sennacherib; which every body must allow was most awful: but for all that, nothing afterwards came to pass; and the bairn that was born, instead of turning out a necromancer or a geni, as we had so much reason to expect, was, from the breast, as silly as a windlestraw. Was not this a plain proof that they are but of a weak credulity who have faith in freats of that kind?

I met, likewise, not in the next year, but in the year after, nearer to this time, another delusion of the same uncertainty. Mrs Gallon, the exciseman's wife, was overtaken with her pains, of all places in the world, in the kirk, on a Sabbath afternoon. They came on her suddenly, and she gave a skirle that took the breath with terror from the minister, as he was enlarging with great bir on the ninth clause of the seventh head of his discourse. Every body stood up. The whole congregation rose upon the seats, and in every face was pale consternation. At last the minister said, that on account of the visible working of Providence in the midst of us, yea in the very kirk itself, the congregation should skail: whereupon skail they did; so that in a short time I had completed my work, in which I was assisted by some decent ladies staying to lend me their Christian assistance; which they did, by standing in a circle round the table seat where the ploy was going on, with their backs to the crying mother, holding out their gowns in a minaway fashion, as the maids of honour are said to do, when the queen is bringing forth a prince in public.

The bairn being born, it was not taken out of the kirk till the minister himself was brought back, and baptized it with a scriptural name; for it was every body's opinion that surely in time it would be a brave minister, and become a great and shining light in the Lord's vineyard to us all. But it is often the will and pleasure of Providence to hamper in the fulfilment the carnal wishes of corrupt human nature. Matthew Gallon had not in after life the seed of a godly element in his whole carcase; quite the contrary, for he turned out the most rank ringing enemy that was ever in our country-side; and when he came to years of discretion, which in a sense he never did, he fled the country as a soldier, and for some splore with the Session, though he was born in the kirk; – another plain fact that shows how little reason there is in some cases to believe that births and prognostifications have no natural connexion. Not that I would condumaciously maintain that there is no meaning in signs sometimes, and may be I have had a demonstration; but it was a sober advice that the auld leddy of Rigs gave me, when she put me in a way of business, to be guarded in the use of my worldy wisdom, and never to allow my tongue to describe what my eyes saw or my ears heard at an occasion, except I was well convinced it would pleasure the family.

'No conscientious midwife,' said she, 'will ever make causey-talk of what happens at a birth, if it's of a nature to work dule by repetition on the fortunes of the bairn;' and this certainly was most orthodox, for I have never forgotten her counsel.

I have, however, an affair in my mind at this time; and as I shall mention no names, there can be no harm done in speaking of it here; for it is a thing that would perplex a philosopher or a mathematical man, and stagger the self-conceit of an unbeliever.

There was a young Miss that had occasion to come over the moor by herself one day, and in doing so she met with a hurt; what that hurt was, no body ever heard; but it could not be doubted that it was something most extraordinar; for, when she got home, she took to her bed and was very unwell for several days, and her een were blear't with greeting. At last, on the Sabbath-day following, her mother foregathert with me in coming from the kirk; and the day being showery, she proposed to rest in my house as she passed the door, till a shower that she saw coming would blow over. In doing this, and we being by ourselves, I speired in a civil manner for her daughter; and from less to more she told me something that I shall not rehearse, and, with the tear in her eye, she entreated my advice; but I could give her none, for I thought her daughter had been donsie; so no more was said anent it; but the poor lassie from that day fell as it were into a dwining, and never went out; insomuch that before six months were come and gone, she was laid up in her bed, and there was a wally-wallying on her account throughout the parish, none doubting that she was in a sore way, if not past hope.

In this state was her sad condition, when they had an occasion for a gradawa at my Lord's; and as he changed horses at the Cross Keys when he passed through our town, I said to several of the neighbours, to advise the mother that this was a fine opportunity she ought not to neglect, but should consult him anent her dochter. Accordingly, on the doctor returning from the castle, she called him in; and when he had consulted the ailing lassie as to her complaint, every body rejoiced to hear that he made light of it, and said that she would be as well as ever in a month or two; for that all she had to complain of was but a weakness common to womankind, and that a change of air was the best thing that could be done for her.

Maybe I had given an advice to the same effect quietly before, and therefore was none displeased to hear, when it came to pass, that shortly after, the mother and Miss were off one morning, for the benefit of the air of Glasgow, in a retour chaise, by break of day, before anybody was up. To be sure some of the neighbours thought it an odd thing that they should have thought of going to that town for a beneficial air; but as the report soon after came out to the town that the sick lassie was growing brawly, the wonder soon blew over, for it was known that the air of a close town is very good in some cases of the asthma.

By and by, it might be six weeks or two months after, aiblins more, when the mother and the daughter came back, the latter as slimb as a popular tree, and blooming like a rose. Such a recovery after such an illness was little short of a miracle, for the day of their return was just ten months from the day and date of her hurt.

It is needless for me to say what were my secret thoughts on this occasion, especially when I heard the skill of the gradawa extolled, and far less how content I was when, in the year following, the old lady went herself on a jaunt into the East Country to see a sick cousin, a widow woman with only a bairn, and brought the bairn away with her on the death of the parent. It was most charitable of her so to do, and nothing could exceed the love and ecstasy with which Miss received it from the arms of her mother. Had it been her ain bairn she could not have dandalized it more!

Soon after this the young lady fell in with a soldier officer, that was sent to recruit in the borough, and married him on a short acquaintance, and went away with him a regimenting to Ireland; but 'my cousin's wee fatherless and motherless orphan,' as the old pawkie carlin used to call the bairn, stayed with her, and grew in time to be a ranting birkie; and in the end, my lord hearing of his spirit, sent for him one day to the castle, and in the end bought for him a commission, in the most generous manner, such as well befitted a rich young lord to do; and afterwards, in the army, his promotion was as rapid as if he had more than merit to help him.

Now, is not this a thing to cause a marvelling; for I, that maybe had it in my power to have given an explanation, was never called on so to do; for everything came to pass about it in such an ordained-like way, that really I was sometimes at a loss what to think, and said to myself surely I have dreamt a dream; for, although it could not be said to have been a case of prognostications, it was undoubtedly one of a most kittle sort in may particulars. Remembering, however, the prudent admonition I had received from the auld leddy of Rigs, I shall say no more at present, but keep a calm sough.

It is no doubt the even-down fact that I had no hand in bringing 'my cousin's wee fatherless and motherless orphan' into the world, but maybe I might have had, if all the outs and ins of the story were told. As that, however, is not fitting, I have just said enough to let the courteous reader see, though it be as in a glass darkly, that my profession is no without the need of common sense in its handlings, and that I have not earned a long character for prudence in the line without ettle, nor been without jobs that cannot be spoken of, but, like this, in a far-off manner.

But it behoves me, before I go farther, to request the reader to turn back to where I have made mention of the poor deserted bairn, Willy Facings; how he was born in an unprepared hurry, and how his mother departed this life, while his ne'er-do-weel father went away like a knotless thread. I do not know how it happened, but come to pass it did, that I took a kindness for the forsaken creature, insomuch that, if his luck had been no better with Miss Peggy Needle, it was my intent to have brought him up with my own weans; for he was a winsome thing from the hour of his birth, and made every day a warmer nest for his image in my heart. His cordial temper was a mean devised by Providence as a compensation to him for the need that was in its own courses, that he would never enjoy a parent's love.

When Miss Peggy had skailed the byke of her cats, and taken Billy, as he came to be called, home to her house, there was a wonderment both in the borough-town and our clachan how it was possible for her, an inexperienced old maid, to manage the bairn; for by this time he was weaned, and was as rampler a creature as could well be, and she was a most prejinct and mim lady. But, notwithstanding her natural mimness and prejinkity, she was just out of the body with love and tenderness towards him, and kept him all day at her foot, playing in the inside of a stool whamled up-side down.

It was the sagacious opinion of every one, and particularly both of the doctor and Mr Stipend, the minister, that the bairn would soon tire out the patience of Miss Peggy; but we are all short-sighted mortals, for instead of tiring her, she every day grew fonder and fonder of him, and hired a lassie to look after him, as soon as he could tottle. Nay, she bought a green parrot for him from a sailor, when he was able to run about; and no mother could be so taken up with her own get as kind-hearted Miss Peggy was with him, her darling Dagon; for although the parrot was a most outstrapolous beast, and skrighed at times with louder desperation than a pea-hen in a passion, she yet so loved it on his account, that one day when it bit her lip to the bleeding, she only put it in its cage, and said, as she wiped her mouth, that it was 'a sorrow.'

By and by Miss Peggy put Billy to the school; but, by that time, the condumacious laddie had got the upper hand of her, and would not learn his lesson, unless she would give him an apple or sweeties; and yet, for all that, she was out of the body about him, in so much that the minister was obligated to remonstrate with her on such indulgence; telling her she would be the ruin of the boy, fine creature as he was, if she did not bridle him, and intended to leave him a legacy.

In short, Miss Peggy and her pet were just a world's wonder, when, at last, Captain Facings, seven years after Billy's birth, being sent by the king to Glasgow, came out, one Sunday to our town, and sent for me to learn what had become of his bairn. Though I recollected him at the first sight, yet, for a matter of policy, I thought it convenient to pretend doubtful of my memory, till, I trow, I had made him sensible of his sin in deserting his poor baby. At long and length I made him to know the blessing that had been conferred by the fancy of Miss Peggy, on the deserted child, and took him myself to her house. But, judge of my consternation, and his likewise, when, on introducing him to her as the father of Billy, whom I well recollected, she grew very huffy at me, and utterly denied that Billy was any such boy as I had described, and foundled over him, and was really in a comical distress, till, from less to more, she grew, at last, as obstinate as a graven image, and was not sparing in the words she made use of to get us out of her habitation.

But, not to summer and winter on this very unforeseen come-to-pass, the Captain and I went to the minister, and there made a confession of the whole tot of the story. Upon which he advised the Captain to leave Billy with Miss Peggy, who was a single lady, not ill-off in the world; and he would, from time to time, see that justice was done to the bairn. They then made a paction concerning Billy's education; and, after a sore struggle, Miss Peggy, by the minister's exhortation, was brought to consent that her pet should be sent to a boarding-school, on condition that she was to be allowed to pay for him.

This was not difficult to be agreed to; and, some weeks after, Bill was accordingly sent to the academy at Green Knowes, where he turned out a perfect delight; and Miss Peggy sent him every week, by the carrier, a cake, or some other dainty. At last, the year ran round, and the vacance being at hand, Bill sent word by the carrier, that he was coming home to spend the time with Mamma, as he called Miss Peggy. Great was her joy at the tidings; she set her house in order, and had, at least, twenty weans, the best sort in the neighbourhood, for a ploy to meet him. But, och hone! when Billy came, he was grown such a big creature, that he no longer seemed the same laddie; and, at the sight of him, Miss Peggy began to weep and wail, crying, that it was an imposition they were attempting to put upon her, by sending another callan. However, she became, in the course of the night, pretty well convinced that he was indeed her pet; and, from that time, though he was but eight years old, she turned over a new leaf in her treatment.

Nothing less would serve her, seeing him grown so tall, than that he should be transmogrified into a gentleman; and, accordingly, although he was not yet even a stripling – for that's a man-child in his teens – she sent for a taylor next day and had him put into long clothes, with top boots; and she bought him a watch, and just made him into a curiosity, that nowhere else could be seen.

When he was dressed in his new clothes and fine boots, he went out to show himself to all Miss Peggy's neighbours; and, it happened, that, in going along, he fell in with a number of other childer, who were sliding down a heap of mixed lime, and the thoughtless brat joined them; by which he rubbed two holes in the bottom of his breeks, spoiled his new boots, and, when the holes felt cold behind, he made his hat into a seat, and went careering up the heap and down the slope with it, as if he had been a charioteer.

Everybody who saw the result concluded that certainly now Miss Peggy's favour was gone from him for ever. But she, instead of being angry, just exclaimed and demonstrated with gladness over him; saying, that, till this disaster, she had still suspected that he might turn out an imposture. Was there ever such infatuation? But, as I shall have to speak more anent him hereafter, I need not here say how he was sent back to the academy, on the minister's advice, just dress'd like another laddie.

TRIBULATIONS OF THE REV. COWAL KILMUN

Chapter I

In the tenth year of my ministry, a very pitiful thing came to pass, the upshot whereof only ended last year, though many, since it happened, have rolled away into the fathomless past.

I was sitting by myself one evening in my study, pondering on the uncertainties of worldly things, when my sister, who was the mistress of the manse, being abroad, one of the serving lasses came in to me and said that a young lady and gentleman were in the parlour wanting a word with me. I rose forthwith, and went to them. They were Mr Ettles and Miss Sylvia Graham. Of her I had no knowledge, though I had heard of whom she had come, and she was not just an unknown stranger.

He was the fifth son of a creditable bonnet laird, not overly well off, by reason of a small family of nine children, and he had been for some time a clerk with his mother's brother, a merchant in Glasgow. The young lady was the dochter of an officer's widow who dwelt in the next parish, and held in much repute by all to whom her excellent qualities were made manifest.

After some short conversation concerning the weather, and the prospects which the kingdom had of a good harvest, Mr Ettles broke the ice of the intent of their visit, by telling me that his uncle had an estabishment, somewhere in America, to which he was appointed to go, a junior partner, and that, as he and Miss Graham had long been trysted, they had resolved to be privately married before he went abroad.

I said that there was no reason to be so hidling about it, which led him to mention that it was not just then expedient to take a wife with him, but that, as soon as he was settled, he intended to write for her.

Something in his manner, when he told me this, made me look at him – I cannot say how – with an eye of compassion. He was a gallant-looking youth, maybe short of one and twenty, with a generous countenance.

Without, however, making him any answer, I turned to Miss Graham, who, if ever I saw a perfect beauty, was surely one. She was younger than him, maybe the best part of two years; but she had the air of a crowned queen with a diadem, and was, in short, a lassie that the Creator had taken pains on in the making of.

I cannot say how it fell out, but the sight of that young and pretty pair made me sorrowful, and I told them they had time enough before them, and that to go through the marriage ceremony then was needless. But Mr Ettles told me many things that bespoke my pity for a sincere and tender heart, and, in short, so persuaded me that I pronounced the blessing on their union, after which I wanted them to stay till my sister would come back, and take tea with us; but they evaded, for he had to go as fast as he could to reach a vessel that night at Greenock. In short, there was nothing in what had been gone through but the making of them one in the eye of God; for, when he left the manse, taking the road to the ferry, Miss Graham went up the glen; and, saving what I had done, they parted seemingly maiden persons.

Why was I dismayed, and boded no good of this mystical marriage, has never been in my power to explain; but the thoughts of it settled down on my heart, and I was sad, and given to meditation concerning it, for many days.

Chapter II

About three months afterwards, one fine day, when the hills were purple and the heavens blue, Miss Graham came over to the manse and gave me, with much satisfaction in her manner, a hint that her jo had reached America, and hoped not to be long of sending for her. The news was very gladdening; and, as she was blithe and spirity, I would not let her away before the gloaming, nor till after she had drunk her tea with us; but the skies became overcast, and the clouds black and lowering, and she was hurried with the apprehension of rain, which came on as it were, with desperation, long before she had reached her mother's dwelling: the result was a wetting to the skin, insomuch that, before getting home, she was ineffectual with cold, and took that night a sore income.

This very great calamity being, in some sort, owing to my blind kindness – for we are erring mortals who know not what we do – I was much troubled about her, and could not think enough of her mysterious marriage, to which I had so innocently, by my tender-heartedness, been led to be art and part.

By and by she seemed to grow better; but still the weight that was on my spirit was not removed; only I had a kind of rejoicing of the mind when I heard she could sit up again. Nevertheless, though I was darkened about her, I should mention that my conscience was very quiet; for surely there was no sin in marrying a handsome young couple that bore God's mark of being made for one another.

During her convalescence, as we thought it was, a letter came about every month from her lawful husband, containing heartening news and blithe encouragements; and before the half-year from his departure was out, he mentioned that he hoped, in the course of the next summer, to be in a way to send for her. Everything was as well as could be expected, only she lingered in her languishment. Still she was in good spirits; for his letters were written in a cordial vein, the free effusions of a heart full of hope, and happy with bright prospects.

I went over to see her every week, and had a satisfaction in conversing with her, for she was of a most mellifluous nature; sometimes, however, I was not quite pleased, for the cold she had taken was very wilful, and in my fears I thought now and then an alteration could be seen upon her. But I did my best to stifle my apprehensions. Alas! they were ordained to prevail; for as the spring came on, there was the visibility of a change that was not manna to my anxieties.

She grew, if it were possible, more and more lovely; but there was a cast in her beauty that was not of this world – a heavenly benignity somehow not delightful to see – that used to make me think sometimes that she was only the vision of a creature 'wearing awa to the land of the leal.'

Her skin became a purer innocence, and the hue of her beautiful cheeks as the dawn of a nearing glory, not yet disclosed to the living children of men. I was often filled with a solemn admiration, when I saw her sitting at the window, in her mother's easy chair, brightening in the setting sun, which seemed to have enjoyment in shining in upon her; but there was a cold sadness, tempering that pleasure, which whiles prompted me to silent prayer that the Lord would be merciful to the flower he had adorned with more beauty than was possessed by the rose of Sharon or the lilies of the field.

At last, one day I went to see her, she complained of not being so well, and was obliged to keep her bed. She said, herself, with her natural sweetness, that she was not very ill, but only wearying for rest.

While the was speaking, a letter came from Mr Ettles, very dolorous for her illness, but rich with glad tidings, stating that, instead of her coming to America alone, he had obtained leave to bring her himself, and would be across the sea in the course of the summer.

Such a letter was delicious to her heart. She got up, and was pleasant with gay thoughts; but, in the midst of her joy, I heard, as it were, her conscious spirit give a hollow sigh, and its echo in my bosom was like an unavailing sorrow, in so much that I was soon after constrained to come away, to hide the despondency that had entered into my inward parts.

Chapter III

But though, for three or four days, her health was refreshed by that letter, and the vivifying hope that it inspired, the langour again returned, in so much that she was confined all day to bed. Her worthy mother became alarmed, and my very night's sleep was molested because of her condition; for it was soon seen that she was in the skeleton embraces of a devouring consumption. She did not, indeed, think so herself, but spoke of Mr Ettles as of a coming joyfulness.

To know the truth and to hear her gaiety was very pitiful; for it was soon seen that the measure of her part and portion in this life was nearly full. But not to dwell on a melancholy without hope, suffice it to say that she suddenly departed into Abraham's bosom one forenoon, leaving the arid wilderness of this world to those who knew her piety and worth, and to the millions of afflicted creatures wherewith it abounds.

In the afternoon I had a thought of going over to sympathize with Mrs Graham, her mother, and dressed myself for that purpose; but before I was just ready, who should come to the manse door, inquiring for me, but Mr Ettles himself from America!

When I heard his voice, for I knew it well, my very living heart lap out of its place, and I was constrained to sit down, and let my tears flow.

Fortunately there was no one in the parlour into which he was shewn, my sister being with Mrs Graham – for her duty as a Christian woman obligated her to be there – and the serving lass that let him in, being of the Celtic tribes, was, of course, not overly sagacious; so, not knowing who he was, she said nothing of what had come to pass, telling him only that I was putting on my clothes, by which I got time to compose myself.

When I had wrestled with and overcome agitation, I went down the stair to Mr Ettles with a fause face, as to hide the worm that was grawing at my heart.

Of course I was well content to see him at first when we met, but said little, and he thinking all was as he expectit, appeared in a manner just carry't; but he stung my heart with an agony, when he said, that for some time he had been haunted with an awful fear, lest any harm had befallen his wedded wife.

I could make no reply; and he continued, saying – 'Ever since I was here that terror has disturbed me; for, when we were standing up receiving your blessing together, I beheld as it were the sudden glare of death look out from her bridal beauty, and I have never been able to away with the omen.'

The very faculty of speech passed from me, which he observing, said –

'There is no accounting for these coincidences.'

At that moment a vehement rush came over my spirit, and I outright burst into sore weeping. The truth indeed of what the Lord had been pleased to do, could be no longer hidden; so that, after some time spent in solemn preparation, I told him that, on that day, at eleven o'clock in the forenoon, Miss Graham, as she was called in this world, was with her Maker in paradise.

Chapter IV

He staid at the manse with me that night; and I did what I could to awaken him to a right sense of the disappointments of this life. Next day, instead of going on to Mrs Graham's, he went back to the ferry, and I heard no more of him till some weeks after, when he was on the point of sailing from Liverpool to America, with, as he said in the letter he wrote to me, 'a withered heart and little wish for the continuance of prosperity.'

For twelve months and more, in the douce solitude of the manse, he was as dead to me. I heard nothing of him; Mrs Graham had not the heart to inquire; but my melancholy concerning him, however, was beginning to be bleached by time; and, at last, when the Occasion was in the neighbouring parish of Demiquigh, Mr Sprose, the minister, having been newly placed, there was a great gathering of folk from ayont the ferry to hear him; by one of whom, from Greenock, a godly captain, I was told that Mr Ettle's uncle was much spoken of, and that it was supposed, he having already stopped payment, that the whole tot of the concern would be sequestered.

The news was not to me glad tidings; for I remembered poor Mr Ettles, and how sore displeasure had fallen on the spring of his life with the shadow of death, in the removal of his virgin wife; and I was as grieved as if I had been a creditor for more than a hundred pounds – ay, much more. But, saving that sorrow, I had little cause to think of him for a long time.

One day, however, as I was taking a stray by myself, meditating on my sermon, and the nothingness of all things in a world of sin and misery, I sat down on a stone on the loch shore, and ruminated of the sun and the seasons, the mysteries of Providence, and the presumption of the narrow discernment of man; marking the gentle flowing in of the tide, as if there was a spirit of love and fondness in nature, willing to embrace all things.

While sitting there, I saw, afar off, a genteel man coming from the ferry, which was no uncommon thing; but there was something in his mien that made me look at him particularly, and, in the end, as he drew near, I discerned it was Mr Ettles. He was coming to see me before, as he said, he would again go abroad; and he then told me that, after his uncle's failure, which caused him to come from America, he had been in a hanging-on state till he had gotten his discharge.

'I am now again clear,' said he, 'and I have formed another connexion with a respectable house.' But he added, with a sigh that dinnled on my heart – 'To me the wine of life is drawn, and I have now but only the lees left.'

We had then some serious conversation anent the same, sitting together on the rocks on the calm sea-shore, with the ancient mountains looking austerely upon us from the other side of the loch, as if taking tent that we deviated into no light discourse.

He then told me that men of the world, who had never been tested with adversity, could not understand the feelings which he felt. 'You,' quoth he to me, 'may, by the help of fancy, have some notion of my bridal blight, and see in it a rational cause of grief; all, too, that might have heard of it would, in some measure, be indulgent to my regret; but the coming on the back of that misfortune, the shipwreck of all the scheme of my endeavours, is what no man can understand, who has not himself had the experience; for there is a searching feeling bred by such events, that goes into the recesses of the bosom, and is as irksome there, as if it were the remorse that waits on a guilty action. They only are able to endure the calamity properly, who reap it as the fruit of endeavours to overreach – a consciousness of having deserved blame mitigates to them the sense of ruin. Yes, let an honest man try what he may, he never can overcome the taint that he has incurred, by being thought to have been either unlucky or imprudent.'

Much of what Mr Ettles said, related to things in a sphere of life whereof I had no knowledge, and I could only exhort him to put his trust in God, and pray for a continuance of his early integrity.

After a considerable sederunt, that was not overly jocund, I rose, thinking he would go with me to the manse; but he said that his time was limited, and having seen me, he would say farewell, and go forward to Mrs Graham's, where he would sleep that night. So we parted; but I was very sorrowful, for the tenor of his discourse made me feel that he was a vessel selected to hold the sour and bitter of life.

What passed with Mrs Graham I never heard: but he staid there all night, and early in the morning was at the ferry, with a sad countenance, as the ferryman's son told me; for he had seen his aching heart manifest in a melancholious look of contemplation, as he rowed him over. 'He was,' said he, 'like one going to a parent's burial.'

Chapter V

For some years after, I heard nothing of Mr Ettles. He was, in a manner, to me, swallowed up in the ocean of mankind, like a drop of the bucket in the great salt sea. But, though where he was, and what he was doing, were hidden from my knowledge, I sometimes thought of him; especially when I heard from the war of neighbour lads among the wounded, and of brave spirits cut down in the bloom and pride of their manhood. In those moments, I saw an afflicting similitude in the lot of the courageous in battle to that of those that are untimely cut down with misfortune.

At times I was grieved at the grief of this thought, for I thought it often unchristian; but a better knowledge was at last vouchsafed unto me, and I was made to discern that valour was a gift implanted for a purpose, though the gifted knoweth not its use; and that even the bloody field of guilty battle was a mean devised by Providence to exalt the human heart.

At first, I was not content for thinking this charity, fearful it might come of my fallen and corrupt nature; and, really, I was angry at myself when I one day saw coming from the ferry an armless soldier, who had gone to the cursed wars in America, then beginning, a proud glorying creature, perfect and sound as he came from the hands of the Maker; for I could not but see he had only earned, with all his bravery, but a stock for the poor trade of begging.

I called to mind the desperate courses of his youth, and tried to persuade myself that war ought to be forbidden by kings and the mighty men of the earth; but, in spite of all, my heart warmed to the visible bankrupt, as I thought him; and I mused of whirlwinds, unmerited humiliations, and the pestilence that walketh in darkness, till I could only say to myself – 'There is a wisdom in the dispensation of war, though we see it not, as there is in all the evils wherewith we are in life afflicted.'

The o'ercome of all these sort of meditations was Mr Ettles. I saw him as an instrument the use whereof could not be found; and, hearing nothing of him, I often marvelled if the purpose of making such a man had yet been revealed; for he was one that could not, somehow, be seen without awe, like an idol of old when it was not in its shrine. The more I thought of him, I thought thus; for, although surely his abortive bridal was a romance of the heart, and his failure a melancholious affair, there was something about the lad himself that made one, like me, unskilled in crafts of the world, think he should have been a grand man. But we are fallen from our sphere, and are struggling amidst uncertainties.

It happened one night, when I had been reflecting much in this aimless manner, seeing mercy where in other times I could only perceive at best but mystery, I went out of the house and stood by myself on the green in front of the manse, looking at the skies and the stars, and thinking of the wonders of time and eternity.

It was a blessed night; and the calm air as holy as if the breath of the spirit of peace had been shed abroad in its serenity. The heavens I thought higher and vaster than common; and the numberless stars as the lamps of the new Jerusalem, and lights in the dwellings of the angels. A religious solemnity was spread over the whole earth, and my thoughts were lifted up.

While standing in this sacred trance, wondering why the all-wise Creator had thought of making such a thing as the world, with that weak entity of presumption, man, to domineer in it, I heard the brushing of a foot in the grass; and, soon after, the weight of a man's hand was laid on my shoulder. Whereupon I turned round, and there was Mr Ettles; behind him, on the gravel before the door, the dark likeness of a stranger loomed in the glimmering – for it could not then be said to be night, but only a thin shadow of the twilight.

Blithe was I to see him, and to shake hands again with one who had so nestled in my remembrance. We then went to the other man, whom he introduced to me as a friend he was much interested in.

'Mr Roslin,' said he, 'came over with me in the same ship. He is a native of the east country, and, being an orphan when he went abroad, is not very sure which way to go till I am at liberty to go with him. As he has no other particular friend, I have brought him to you – though myself, in intercourse with you, but almost a stranger; confident that you will make him welcome for a short time till I look about me.'

This introduction was more remarkable for the terms in which it was made, than in itself; though, in that respect, I thought it by common. I said, however, that I was well pleased to see and to entertain anybody Mr Ettles brought; and then remembering what he said about looking about him, I made a conjecture to myself that he was again drifting on the wide world. But I said nothing; only invited them both into the manse, where for a time we had a curious discourse about the foreign land they had come from; and I made a thanksgiving for their safe return; after which we retired to our several places of rest.

Chapter VI

I never closed an eye that night; for I was sorely troubled in mind about Mr Ettles; as I thought him, by what he had said, a young man ordained for disasters. Yet, saving this inadvertency about looking about him, he had given me no reason to think that adversity had in any shape meddled with him.

In the morning, we had a jocose breakfast, somewhat early, as Mr Ettles intended to go by the second boat across the ferry, meaning to travel to Glasgow that day; which he did, leaving Mr Roslin to bide with me till he could return.

This Mr Roslin was an elderly man, with a bald head, a contented countenance, and peering eyes, that denoted an inquisitive spirit. After Mr Ettles went away, we walked forth to the hills together, and had a very instructive conversation concerning many things, and especially of the uncertainty that hovered in life. But, though he was not overly orthodox, there was a solid ingredient of Christianity in much of what he did say, pleasant to hear; and he preaching resignation and contentment, like an apostle or a gospel minister.

From Mr Roslin, I learned with a dismayed heart, that the bad luck which kythed to Mr Ettles in his green years, had been permitted to pursue him up and down, and that he was but little better in a worldly sense than when he left his native land. He likewise told me that, finding he was trafficking to little purpose, and the hope of brightening growing dimmer as he grew older, he had come to a resolution to pull in his horns, and make, as Mr Roslin called it, his orbit of a narrower scope. 'Which,' he added, 'I was sorry to hear; for a man that changes his conduct on resolution undergoes no change at all, though to himself the change seem great. Poor Ettles will be still the same, and the world will think so too. He will reap only the pains of perseverance; and find out, when too late, the original sin of thinking he could make himself wiser than he was created.'

This led me to remark, in reply, that the early observance of a predominance of resolution in the mind of Mr Ettles knit him to my affections and anxieties; for his barren bridal with Miss Graham was of that nature – taking, as it were, a security from Providence that she should be his wife.

Mr Roslin had never heard of that pitiful disappointment, and was very concerned when I told him the particulars; saying – 'However, it was but a foretaste of what Ettles has experienced; for, although, of all men I ever saw, he is the least given to rashness, yet he meditates in secret of his purposes, and decides on adopting what he does, in a manner that surprises his best friends. When he has wrought himself into a resolution, the little good will be beggared, and yet not have turned him. He seems as pliant as a rush in the breeze: as pliant he is; but, once broken, he can never grow whole again.'

I cannot explain the impression which the conversation with Mr Roslin in that first walk had upon me. It deepened into the very quick every recollection of Mr Ettles traced upon my memory, from the evening of the mystical marriage; and, without even a show of any reason, made me think of him with more solicitude. However, little passed afterwards about him, while Mr Roslin staid at the manse, which was fully three weeks; but I pondered a great deal on what had passed; for, in the town of a country parish, a misfortunate man is a great unco, and I could not but think Mr Ettles was one, though he was still young, with the air and promise of prosperity. But I have seen the apple tree with all its flourishes cut down in the spring, and said in my heart, 'Wherefore were those blossoms?'

When Mr Ettles returned to take Mr Roslin away, he was persuaded by me to stop a few days at the manse, during which I hoped to discern something of that change which I thought must be visible upon him; but I saw none – only he never went to see Mrs Graham, nor minted a syllable of her daughter. On the morning, however, before he went away, seeing me taking my morning stray in the glebe, he came to me alone, and we had a few weighty words together. I say weighty; for what Mr Roslin had told me of the nature of his resolutions, when cooled and chrystalized, made me very acute.

Chapter VII

'Well, Mr Ettles,' quo' I, as he came towards me, 'so you are resolved to go to-day; but you have not said a word about when I am to see you again.'

'It is because I do not know myself. If wishes were of any avail, it would not be long; for I am wearying for rest, and I think the bed for it is in a manse – or the kirkyard; but the machinery of Providence is very self-willed, and our inclinations can seldom influence its movements.'

'Never,' said I, seriously: 'we but think we do, when we see the wheels going the way we wish; but excuse me, Mr Ettles, if I inquire, with the freedom of an old friend, have you come to any determination?'

He looked at me for a short time, thoughtfully – at last, smiling, said, 'Mr Roslin has been talking then about me?' And he added, briskly – 'I do not think I have met with much very uncommon; but, even little as it may be thought, it begets suggestions which those who know it not cannot imagine. It makes one sharp to see and keenly to feel; but the hypocrisy is ineffectual, for the world will not allow that there can be any change. It will still judge by the estimate it made of one in youth, without experience: few understand that alteration of which a man is himself conscious.'

As he said this, I thought of what Mr Roslin had remarked concerning resolutions, and the obduracy of his: but I made no reply, for he speedily continued –

'I had a high and beautiful hope. It was soon quenched; but another, almost as bright and fair, arose. It was, in appearance, perhaps, as brilliant, but it failed to excite that desire which is the life of ambition. At last, it was obscured, and tarried dimly in a watery cloud. Much of the charm of life soon vanished; and I could only ask, "What is to be our recompense for having been born at all?" No, Sir, the vanity of life is over – I have abandoned and forsworn the pursuit of its gauds. I will never more think of aspiring to rise; and I have resolved not to fall lower than – death.'

I shuddered at the expression, and sighed with much sorrow.

'Most people,' he resumed, 'set a false value on the best things in life: I have accustomed myself to think of the worst familiarly; – suffering is but for a few days.'

'Mr Ettles,' said I, slowly, to make a deep impression, 'you have not thought of disgrace.'

'Perhaps not,' was his reply, after a pensive pause; and then he added hurriedly, 'but death can extinguish the sense of it.'

'Your words are wild,' was my answer. 'In the name of God, what have you resolved to do?'

'To live – to do the best I can.'

Just then, one of the serving lasses came to the door and made a signal to us that breakfast was ready. So we hastened back to the manse, our conversation being so interrupted.

After breakfast, and a hurried morning exercise, was over, we walked all three to the ferry, where I bade them adieu in a cordial manner. But, as they stepped into the boat, Mr Roslin gave me a significant look, which shewed he had made a conjecture anent what had passed between me and Mr Ettles in the glebe. Then the boat rowed away, and I returned home in an unaccountable perplexity.

There surely was no earthly reason why I should be so concerned about Mr Ettles. What was he to me? Neither kith nor kin; and although I was, may be, art and part in his romantical marriage with Miss Graham, that was an old story, and, by rights of time, should have been forgotten.

Then I thought of his familiarity with me, and how he took enfoeffment of my regards from the very first; for he was then a blithe birky, with Miss Graham at his side, who was indeed a lily of a young lady, that ought not to have died; but her Maker had use for her in his mansions – blessed be the name of the Lord!

All that day I was in a manner demented, and it was lucky for me that Miss Becky, my sister, was throng in the kitchen, with her jellies or her jams – I forget which, for my mind was in a state of anarchy and confusion – and she saw not what made me dismal. Towards tea-time, however, we had visiters – salt-water folk – to whom I was bound to be civil, as they had come across the loch to see me.

Being obliged to make an exertion, I was, by the time of their departure, in my usual; but ever and anon the thought of Mr Ettles came uppermost, although I had nothing more to do with him than a common Christian man has with a fellow creature that lays a rightful cess on our sympathy.

Chapter VIII

It might be a month after Mr Ettles went away, taking Mr Roslin with him, that I was sitting on my usual seat on the mossy stone near the shore, thinking of the wonderful plenishment of the earth, my thoughts solaced by the benevolence that then invested all around with peacefulness. Miss Becky had gone over the ferry in the morning, to buy something, and to bide all night with the Rev Dr Dozent and his sister – a woman of a fashious kind, that I did not like, or I would have gone too.

Sitting there by myself, in a meditating posture, the ferry lad came towards me with a letter in his hand, seeking payment of the postage, which, by its heaviness, I knew had come from London.

Not having a sufficiency in my pouch, I rose and went back with him, to get the needful at the manse; for it was pactioned with my sister, that, whenever she went afield, she should leave some change always for outfalls, ready in a strouples teapot that we keepit for the purpose.

When I had settled with Hector for the price, I then opened the letter, and, lo and behold! it was from Mr Ettles! But what he said may be gotten from his own penmanship better than from any precise I can make thereof.

London.

> My Dear Friend, – I am *yet* vain enough to think you will be glad to hear of me; and I write this to let you know that I have carried my resolution, to remain sequestered from the busy world, into effect. A distant relation, desirous of retiring, has been induced to dispose of the good-will of his moderate

business to me; and last week I was installed in his shop –

The world forgetting, by the world forgot.

My next object will be to find a suitable wife as soon as possible. The only obstacle, indeed, to my final settlement, is the want of sufficient means to make some provision for her in the event of my death; for I regard this as indispensable: – without it, marriage, in my eyes, loses all its sanctity. It will probably be soon settled; for my hopes of happiness are beneath the ground.

I do not intend to be very chary either as to beauty or accomplishments: the walk I have now entered does not require that I should. Respectability is all I shall look for; but I shall marry like a prince – for policy. To you I need not say more – the grass grows green on the reason which influences me.

Mr Roslin is still with me, and sends his best respects to you and the kind Miss Becky.

Believe me, truly yours,

Alex. Ettles.

N.B. – It will oblige me if you could find time to say what you think, now that I am fixed, of the course I have adopted.

The letter was short; but, coming from whom it did, it was to me full of matter.

First and foremost, a letter from Mr Ettles, and all the way from London, was a thing that never entered my head to expect; and I could not but jalouse that there was something in it more than met the ear. Then, what had I to do with his getting good-wills of businesses? He was in a manner a stranger to me; and how could he think I would care to hear of it?

But, for all the indifferency that I would fain have cherished, the tidings to my heart were not gospel, nor fraught with gladness; in short, I became very sad, and said, as it were, with an inspiration in which I had no volition – 'So this is the end of him that seemed fashioned for great purposes!' And I shed a tear, thinking of buds that are blasted.

When I had meditated long on the first clause, I then took up the second. I hope there is no wrong in saying that I thought it overly worldly; for what would become of the command to increase and multiply, if every man put off his marriage till he was in a condition to make a settlement? I disapproved of it; and so I meant to tell him, and to say that the crows are wily and far-casting, but wha ever heard of them, or any of God's creatures, making marriage-settlements?

The third paragraph seemed to me, as it were, gritty – a tear mingled with sand; and had it not been for the green-grass reason, which was eloquent to the heart of one that had seen Miss Graham, I would have been evendown angry with him.

But the postscript was mystical over all; for it seemed to me to say that he was not well satisfied with himself, or he would not have thought of asking for my approval; for it needs not the whole wisdom of the General Assembly to teach me that, when a man has done a turn, and seeks an opinion of it afterwards, he wants but to hear approbation, being doubtful himself if he has done right. And so I told him in my answer, but in a gentle and far-off way; for when I rose in the morning, his letter only inspired pity and compassion. I was, indeed, much cast down, and the reason of it was to myself a mystery.

Chapter IX

For more than twelve months, I heard nothing of Mr Ettles; and I began to think he had maybe taken it ill that I had been so free with him; still, somehow, I could not imagine how he might do that; for what I said was in sincerity, and my real sentiments, well folded up in Christian delicacy. However, about the end of a year, I got two letters by one post from London. The one was from Mr Ettles – just a bit line, telling me he was that day married to a woman; and the other was in a frank from Mr Roslin, anent the same job, giving me all the particulars. Of Mr Ettles' letter of notification I shall say nothing; but Mr Roslin's was well deserving of being recorded; and here it is: –

London.

My Dear Sir, – Although I have been long of writing you, I have ever retained a very warm remembrance of the apostolic simplicity of your character. Perhaps, however, I might not yet have had this pleasure; but a friend has given me a frank, by which I can let you know, without cost, of an event which took place this morning, in which I am sure, you will be interested.

Our friend Ettles, in pursuance of a *resolution*, has been

married. His choice seems, as far as connexions are concerned, to have been judicious.

The lady has been bred, perhaps, too retired for him. She talks, however, very wisely; but I think that I have seen that she does not act quite so discreetly as might be expected from the tenor of her conversation; being a little like Charles the Second –

Who never said a foolish thing, and never did a wise one.

I speak to you frankly; because I am sure that whatever affects his happiness is very dear to you; and I remain, respectfully yours,

James Roslin.

This, it must be allowed by every one, was a curt epistle; and it caused me to have divers reflections, which, as always is the case in similar instances, were not to the advantage of the writer. This jealousy, as I must acknowledge it was, came not, however, of my nature, but was learned at college with my other learning; it, therefore, soon passed, like the shadow of the summer cloud on the face of the loch; and I was soon restored to myself again, but, in a manner, obligated to put several questions to my own mind respecting Mr Roslin.

Who is he? – how comes it that he takes such an interest in what pertains to Mr Ettles? – and what could make him so very explanatory about the disagreeables of the bride? For what he said was not opiatical to my anxieties; not that he was evendown with his condemnation, but it was very plain he had a sediment of anxiety in his bosom that Mr Ettles had been more governed in his choice by a resolution to settle himself, than by judgment, or taste, or a consideration for his own habitudes.

When I had pondered some time – it might be the best part of the afternoon, for the ferry-boat comes over at one, post meridian, and I was still sitting, in my inward soliloquy, when my sister said that the tea was ready – not having exchanged words with her at dinner, but only saying the grace at it. I drank none, however, but rose and walked abroad to refresh my spirit, as my wont was, in trouble of mind, with a sober communing with the mountains; the staid aspect of which, like that of grey-headed elders, never failed to conjure me into composure, if I needed it. Only for that, as well as for other mysteries, were the hills of the Highlands fashioned in the palms of the hands of divine wisdom.

Wherefore I was so vexed, after having come to a conclusion that Mr Roslin was a discreet, decent man, is not to be told; far less how I was so affected with the blithesome news of a wedding, betokening a fulfilment of the early command concerning the plenishing of the earth; but so it was – the news of that day were not to me blithesmeat, and yet I could not say the cause thereof.

After a season, and in the hallowed tranquillity of the twilight, I returned home, and told Becky – who had seen I was fashed at something – that our friend, Mr Ettles, was again married, and that I had a letter from Mr Roslin; without saying anything to her of what it was about. She remarked, however, that I had visibly gotten a drug that had sickened me.

In time, the wound I had received – for I can call it no better – skinned over, though the part was aye tender; for never could I bear to think that a putting on of the conjugal yoke upon resolution, was according to Scripture, or could kythe in better than heart-burning and affliction.

Chapter X

For several months, nothing particular happened – only, it being known to the Presbytery that the dining-room in the manse needed painting, I was, of course, chosen to go into the General Assembly while it was doing; being subject, at times, when I took a cold, to a shortness of breath, for which the smell of the paint was not a condiment. And, going into Edinburgh on the solemn business of the Church who should I meet with there but Mr Roslin? who, having nothing upon his hands, had come down from London to see how the Assembly was conducted.

He was most glad to see me; and we had more than two words about Mr Ettles, whom, he told me, he hoped was happy. I did not like to hear of that hope, for it seemed to intimate a fear. Moreover, he agreed with me that a marriage on resolution was not on a proper principle; adding – for he was an auld-headed man – that, although Mr Ettles was able for all things, it was not easy to say what he was fit for; being overly obdurate in sticking to his own opinion, even when most complaisant to that of others.

'It is a sore pity that he is so,' quo' Mr Roslin; 'for his wife is as obdurate as he is; and in every house and state there must be a head:

the rule and power must either be with the wife or the man – it cannot abide with both. However, ye will be able shortly to judge for yourself; for Mr and Mrs Ettles are coming to Scotland, and I know he intends to visit you, for whom he cherishes a regard as sincerely as if he really hated you, and had resolved to love you.'

The expectation of seeing Mr Ettles was as the springtime; and I walked every blessed morning to the pier of Leith, to inquire, at the smacks, if he was yet come; but he came not – and, when the General Assembly broke up, I returned to my own parish, with the sense of a cold in my heart, being the sense of a disappointment. The complaint did not however, afflict me long; for, in the month of August after, he and his wife came to the manse, soakit with rain. In coming over the ferry, a desperate thunder-plump fell from the heavens, and they were caught in the jaw of it, to which an even-down pour was a moderation. I mind it very well; for it was so inordinate, that it caused me, before they came, to put up an ejaculation for the poor beasts of the field, and the birds of the air, in which the dumb fish of the deep sea were not forgotten.

After they had shifted themselves – for they were past drying – we had some mutual conversation; gay it was, but not of a satisfactory solidity. I could discern, however, with the tail of my eye, that my sister was greatly taken with Mrs Ettles, who, she said privately to me in her transports, in the course of the evening, 'was a most delightful creature.' In conscience, however, I could not go so far; though I will not positively deny that she was void of merit. But I thought of Miss Graham, with a shaking head, and I looked at Mr Ettles, still in his promising years, saying to myself – 'Verily, Providence clotheth itself in a mantle of perplexities.'

As they took us anawares, we had not a by-ordinar' dinner that day; for everybody knows that a well-ordered manse is no a galravitching hotel in Edinburgh. But, after dinner, the ladies went away; and, as I heard afterwards, Mrs Ettles unpacked her trunk to see that nothing was wet, and showed Becky such paraphernauls as she had no notion of. Mr Ettles sat with me, and we had some neighbour-like discourse together; but the upshot of it darkened my spirit; for I could see that much of his winsomeness, when here with Miss Graham, had taken the wings of the morning; and, though he might be glegger, he was an altered man, with a ponderosity, now and then, in what he said, that I could only think was diseased wisdom.

After a this and that, of no particularity, he began to tell me he did not think it was ordained that man or woman could ever love more than once; but I told him that I knew many most sensible and discreet persons who married three times. 'Ay,' said he – 'I don't doubt it; but once for love, and twice for expediency' – by which we were led on, by a circumbendibus, to speak of himself; when he made an observation most astounding.

'Love,' said he, 'is an instinct implanted by the Creator: but resolution is the offspring of human reason, the flavour of the forbidden fruit. When we obey instincts, we earn happiness; but when we listen to reason, we are allured into suffering and sorrow, for reason is but the use of our knowledge of good and evil.'

No more then passed; for, the ladies coming in, we were obligated to be jocose; but his words dwelt on my remembrance.

Chapter XI

In the course of time, on that night when Mr Ettles and his new wife came to see us, we all went to bed; but, before I left Becky, she began to tell me what a pleasant woman the lady was, and what a fortune her father had settled on her to make them comfortable.

I did not like to hear this, and recollected how Mr Roslin had likened her, in his letter, to the runagate king; thinking she surely was at a loss for discourse, to speak even to anybody, of what her father had done or could do; and I went away sorrowful.

I could not help thinking that there was something in the indiscretion of Mrs Ettles that could not be very agreeable to the proud heart of her husband, if he knew it; for, although it was plain he had married on resolution, he was not such a sordid character as was ever likely to marry for the lucre of gain: and I thought it was a warning, though I could not say why, to all young women, to take good care never to put it in their husbands' power to suspect that it was possible for them to imagine that they had only married them for money; for man is a proud animal, and does not like, whatever may be his faults, to be thought meanly of.

From the little I knew of Mr Ettles, and the less I did of his wife, this bragging of her fortune was an omen that boded no augmentation to their happiness; for, though, no doubt, marriages have been made both by men and women for settlements, there has generally been something more looked to than mere money; and I was sure that

Mr Ettles had another spoke in the wheel of his matrimony than it. However, I fell asleep, resolving to have my eyes open when I awoke, and to wise on the conversation to a disclosure; for now I began to think something was on the mind of Mr Ettles, which, perhaps, could be explained.

Next morning, the lift was bright and the earth all glittering, in so much that, although I did not forget my intention to probe the gathering visible in the bosom of Mr Ettles, my heart was not so set on it as it was in the watches of the night; and therefore I postponed my resolution to a more convenient season. Thus it came to pass that I did not trouble him at all with my scrupulosities; for the weather grew better, and the two days of his visitation were given to enjoyment – only there was one thing most touching, which fell out on the afternoon afore the day of his departure with the woman he had married.

When me and him had solaced ourselves with a tumbler after dinner, he proposed, as the day without was most enticing, that we should take a walk. Accordingly, as I am a man always for temperance, we went forth; and, in our easy, leisurely manner, talking of many things, and nothing important, I found ourselves on the road to Mrs Graham's dwelling, that had been. Thinking he might be minded to call there, for auld langsyne, I said to him, stopping suddenly – 'Mr Ettles,' quo' I, 'I jalouse ye are no acquaint with what has happened!'

'No,' replied he; 'what has?'

'Mrs Graham,' said I, with a melancholious voice, 'was removed last Lammas, and now sleeps with her daughter. We should lay it to heart.'

He made no answer for some time; but I saw there was a going-on in his breast that could not be very pleasant. By and by, however, he spoke, saying – 'No matter, we can go to the churchyard.' And he walked forward, I following, really a dejected object; for I could not but think of one that had been most dear to him, and the blight which had early fallen on all his prospects.

In all the way to the kirkyard, which was then a long mile from the spot where I had corrected him, he never opened his lips, and I had nothing to say; for, though it was then the eye of summer, there was the shadow of a cloud still on my spirit, and I wondered of what would ensue; for he was then a married man, and I had some doubt if it wasna just right, meditating among the tombs when he had a living wife, though maybe she was not worthy to hold the candle to her who was the bride that bedded with the worm.

When we reached the kirkyard, the yett was shut, which obligated us to clamber over the dyke; in the doing whereof, I mind that the left knee of a new pair of black breeks, that I had put on for an honesty that day, was torn; and that I fell among burrs and nettles, which grew hard by, seemingly of as little use as heritors, who are permitted to be for a fashion, and might be well weeded away without detriment to parish ministers, especially when dining-rooms in manses need painting.

Chapter XII

Being, after my calamity, over the dyke, we walked sedately to where Mrs Graham and her daughter were laired in cold and silence; and when I had shewn him the graves, I left him to his soliloquies; telling him, in order that there might be no mistakes, 'That highest and greenest of the twa hillocks was the last hap of the old lady. The other grave,' said I, 'is a monumental emblem of the memory of man: it's in a state of obliteration, as the image of her that slumbers beneath it is in the minds of those who are yet of this world.'

I then left him, and went about among the headstones, reading the epitaphs on many a frail memorial erected nigh; which, for the most part, were no doubt penned with a regard to veracity. One, however, I did meet with, which in conscience I could not approve; for how could the schoolmaster, who penned the same, tell what virtue and seemliness, as he said, were about the man whom he had never known in this life, nor heard even his name mentioned after death, as the sprose on the stone shewed forth. The fact was, that, one morning in winter, after a midnight mixture and jumbling of the winds and the waves, the drowned body of a genteel man, with a gold watch, and money in his purse, was found upon the shore; which, as it behoved the parish to bury, was done in a Christian-like manner. The valuables were given to me to keep till an inheritor would cast-up; but, after two years, none appeared, and Mr Beta, the schoolmaster, then proposed that his son, who was just out of his time as a mason, should make a headstone, as there was a fund to come and go on. To this I could see no reasonable objection. Accordingly, a very shapely headstone was hewn; but, before setting it up, the young man pointed out to me that it would be daftlike to have a monument without an inscription; so I told him to get his father to write one. The old dominie thought, however, that, as the stranger was unknown, a plain, simple headstone was quite suitable; and, consulting me, I was of the same opinion; but Tom, the mason, said that there never was such a thing heard of as a monument saying nothing – in short, it would be just a masonic dumbie, to put it up as it was; adding that, as there were plenty of funds in my hands, there could be no reason that the headstone should be a non-entity. So, to keep quiet in the land, I authorized his father to indite a becoming epitaph; and Tom engraved it, grumbling, however, at the shortness of the job; for he was paid by the lettering.

Till that day, I had never seen what was on the stone; and well pleased I was not, when I read such evendown trash, and so much of it, as that graceless creature, Tom, persuaded his father to write for his benefit. Indeed, I was wroth at the havers, and determined on the spot to have the nonsense hewn out and extirpated utterly; but, somehow, one thing after another has come in the way, and the headstone is still standing there, a laughing-stock to everybody that happens to see it. Few, however, are guilty of going, in this life, to so melancholious a place as our kirkyard, either to the molestation of auld Peggy Rankine's cow, that feeds in it, or to moralize on the headstones.

When I had smoothed my birses, after the perusal of the Dominie's paternoster anent the incognito virtues of the unknown man, I went back to Mr Ettles, to see if he was done; and, still without speaking, he took hold of me by the arm, and walked me to the dyke, over which we came into the highway, an accident I was greatly surprised at; for, if I had recollected it, there would have been no need for us to have clambered the wall, or to split the knee of my best breeks, to say nothing about falling among nettles and gulbroch, which is not pleasant, and far from being odoriferous herbage.

All the way back to the manse, Mr Ettles was still taciturn; in so much, that his wife noticed it when we were drinking our tea, and said, that she was none surprised to see him 'so glum after looking at his old sweetheart's grave;' for, it seems, she had seen us in the kirkyard, while she was taking a walk on the croft with Becky, my sister; who would not let her disturb us, being a woman of a compassionate nature, and really not so idolatrous of Mrs Ettles as she had been at first, notwithstanding her proper style of the English language, and her beautiful silk gown, trimmed with orange ribands.

Chapter XIII

In the evening, after tea, me and Mr Ettles were sitting very soberly together by ourselves, having a solid conversation concerning the difference in the physiognomy of coming and going Time; no doubt the consequence of his rumination at the door of the narrow house of Miss Graham; and he said that nothing disturbed him so much as to see that the companions of his youth seemed to think, after all he had borne, that he was still the same whom they had formerly known.

'I know,' said he, 'that some think, with reason, when a man resolves to change, he does not change at all – and my friend, Mr Roslin, is of that opinion – but they forget that we are creatures of circumstances, and that a change of circumstances forces on a change of character. I agree that when a man resolves, of himself, to become different from what he was, it is very doubtful if any alteration can be effected; but when resolution comes in aid of new circumstances, the effect may be very great indeed: – such is the case with me. The morning of my life was bright – the flowers in my path, oh, so beautiful! Fortune seemed to beckon me on; and, without vanity, I may say, that a conscious activity spurred me into enterprise. But the sun became soon clouded, the flowers withered, fickle fortune flew away; and the activity now is apt to fall into fits of absence, and forget the seeming destination that once stimulated its energy. I live no longer for the world – I but endure life.'

This was very recondite to me; and I did not well know what to say; but, all things considered, I reflected that it could not be far wrong to observe, 'I was sorry to think he was not just as happily married as he might have been.'

He looked at me seriously for some time, and then said –

'The change had come upon me before I thought of marrying. It should, therefore, be regarded as a consequence of having abdicated ambition. The motives existed no longer which formerly influenced me, and could not enter into the considerations which induced me to submit to the conjugal yoke. However, to answer your remark more directly, I have only to complain of what I believe most married men do – namely, that perhaps my wife does not clearly enough see that her own happiness would be augmented, if she thought more of mine; but it would cause trouble to her to do so; and it is the nature of the female mind to act more from inclination than duty, though it always thinks its sense of duty is paramount. A man is a more dutiful animal than a woman; but he says less about it.'

Much more of the like discourse passed between us, and what Mr Ettles said was less intelligible to me; but two things increased my perplexity.

First, How he, Ettles, came to make me such a depositary of his secret feelings, who was, in a manner, a stranger to him. And,

Second, How I came to be so constrained against my will to be entangled with his tribulations; for, after that visit, they multiplied, and I thought of them the more and more.

It was plain that both me and Mr Roslin were in the mist concerning him; and so, when he and Mrs Ettles went away to England next day, I resolved to keep a gleg watch upon his fate and courses, he being a phenomenon such as the pastor of a country parish has it not at all times in his power to contemplate. His wife, I saw, was a mere woman; but he was a curious engine in the arsenal of Providence, of which the use was not yet discerned. Surely, indeed, it was a matter to suggest reflection, that a living man should account himself an implement of no use; and much and often I thought of that circumstance, saying, with reverence, that whoever has worldly functions left, has visibly worldly tasks to perform.

Upon the whole, the visit from Mr and Mrs Ettles was a visitation; and I was some time, many days, after their departure, no just myself, by thinking about them; wondering how folk that seemed so like the rest of the world, could have that within which was so different. Of the wife, however, I did not cogitate much; for she was – what my sister said in her jocosity – a broth-and-beef character; whereas he was – as she likened also – a Pace-and-Yule dainty, whereof the ingredients could not be bought in every grocery shop, and, in the cooking, needed mair cunning than his leddy had power, she feared, to put forth.

Chapter XIV

It was fully the best part of half-a-year, from the time Mr and Mrs Ettles were with us, that, one wintry morning, Mr Roslin, who was in no sort of manner more than an acquaintance, and no an intimate one, came across the ferry to see me. Well do I mind the weather; for, although it might be then past the dead of the year, the winter was not, for weeks after, out of the dead thraws. The morning was bleak and the blast easterly, and there was a sprinkling of snow and hail on the tops of the hills, that betokened more of wind and wet than a solid rigour. In short, it was just as if winter were angry to think that spring was coming, and gowled her away.

Mr Roslin, it seems, had been detained at Greenock for some time, by a foul south-west wind; and everybody knows that Greenock, which is dreadfully addicted to south-westers, is, when they soak, a most wearisome place. He was then going back to the Americas – the stramash having ended in their independence; and, having nothing to do, thought he would come over to see me. But he paid dear for his pastime. The wind, which had been long squally from the south-west, changed into the easterly airt when he was in the ferry-boat; and when he left me to return to the ship in which he had taken his passage, she had availed herself of the easterly wind and sailed without him; which was surely a most hard thing, he having paid his passage. But no better could be expected; for the Yankees are not a people of a principle, not having an Establishment. It is hoped, however, that, in time, a candle will be lighted among them.

Mr Roslin, on his arrival at Greenock, finding he had missed his passage, was far demented; and sent me a scrape of a pen, to let me know his condition, and how his trunks were gone, and with them all his money – which, I understood, was in a kind of foreign coin called the ready – begging me to lend him a small supply, till he could hear from London.

I cannot say that I was pleased with this; and Becky was most peremptory in saying he should have no money, knowing, as we did, so little of him; adding, likewise, that surely he had a stock of impudence to think of applying to the like of us. But, when I came to think of him, a forlorn stranger in such a metropolitan place as Greenock, the carnality of my heart softened, and I had some doubts if it would be just Christian to let him perish in the streets of that town for lack of a morsel. The upshot was, that I resolved to go to Greenock myself, and if I found him in an extremity, to break the back of a guinea-note upon him. Becky, however, was of opinion that I should take no notice of his letter at all; for, she said his writing to me was either an accident or offence, like those malefactions of which she read of in the newspapers, when she happened, now and then, to get the loan of one. Nevertheless, the more I thought of my duty, the more my feelings thawed; and, at last, out of a constraint of obligation, next day, I went to Greenock, so noted as it is for wet weather.

The mercy of Providence was very visible when I took my departure across the ferry; for the day was fine, and the lift as clear as a blithe lassie's glad blue eye. But nothing is steadfast in the howling wilderness.

As was to be expected, just as I got in sight of Greenock, it began to pour as if all the powers of the air had watering cans in their hands, watering, and the earth a hesp laid out to be bleached. In short, when I got to the inn where Mr Roslin put up, I was sorely steepit, all dripping – and, as I may say now in jocosity, no a roast of beef either. Umbrellas were not then created.

By the time I got to the inns, Mr Roslin had done with his dinner, and I catched him drinking wine out of a decanter, by himself; a thing I never evened my hand to, in the most disconsolate solitude.

He was glad to see me, however, as he said, and seemingly could not make enough of me; calling for a glass of brandy, which, he said, was better for my humidity than cold wine; and when I told him how I had come on purpose to temper, as it were, his affliction, he said that it was the very thing he thought I might do. Indeed, his gladness and sympathy, I'll never deny, put me on my guard; for the man, said I, inwardly, that makes ower muckle of you, has either cheated you or intends it; – so, notwithstanding I was as jocose as could be with Mr Roslin, I joined, in the words of Scripture, trembling with my mirth.

When I had taken the brandy, dried myself, and got the residue, as Mr Roslin said, of his dinner – which might have been a reasonable banquet for the Duke and Sir Alexander – I opened the intent and purpose of my coming; the which, however, I must defer to another chapter.

Chapter XV

First and foremost, I began with a far-off moralizing anent the uncertainties of this life, and the troubles that man is born to, as the sparks fly upward; which Mr Roslin fully admitted was most true; adding, in a concerned way, that he had tasted the lot of human nature more acutely since his return to Scotland than he had ever thought to have done.

'All,' said he, 'that I formerly knew, when I went abroad more than fifty years ago, are gone. I was a stranger in the very settlement of my home – village I should call it; there was not one being that I ever heard of. The very minister, an old, venerable, grey-headed man, was removed, and two, successively after his death, had filled his place.'

'That,' I replied, 'no doubt accounts for your destitute condition; all your friends being away, I really do not wonder at your dolorosity.' But, although I spoke most sympathisingly, I girded my loins, and set a watch on the door of my lips, especially when he said –

'Now, this visit is most kind, and could not have been expected; and yet it is no more than what I thought might be. Something runs before me, that I am not to be long for this world; and, having nothing to do, waiting for your answer to my letter, I have been amusing myself in writing an outline of my will.'

'That was very odd,' quo' I, pushing my chair back.

'It was so; and here it is. Among other friends whom I have learned to esteem in life, you will find yourself mentioned for a small token of my regard.'

He then read: – 'And, in testimony of the impression which his apostolic simplicity has made upon me, I request the Rev. Cowal Kilmun to accept of one hundred dollars, to buy a ring, and to wear it as a memorial of one who believed him to be a pattern of honesty and truth.'

I looked at his feet; but his shoes were like other people's; nevertheless, I thought, if he had cloots, he might hide them. Oh! I was feared; saying to myself, 'Surely the devil can do no good.'

We then diverged into a less particular subject; and, when it was about time to take a cup of tea, he ordered it in, and shook me cordially by the hand, saying, that, although he did wish I would visit him, it was a romance he had never expected to see fulfilled.

Afterwards, he became more like mortality; and my dread wore off, insomuch, that I thought him a very sensible man, especially when he mentioned that he did not intend to apply to me for any money, till he heard from London; by which I saw there would be time enough to mediate how best to jook him, before he calculated on being in need.

Thus, from one thing to another, till it was far in the night – the weather no mending, of course, for we were in Greenock – we grew into better acquaintance; and I had my doubts at last, if I had done him even scrimp justice.

Towards ten o'clock, we resolved to part for the night; and I was shewn to my bed-room, leaving him behind. About the small hours, I heard him also going to his room; and, soon after, I fell asleep, never thinking that anything could be amiss; for, although I was not at first content with him in my own breast, that dubiety had worn off towards the heel of the evening; and when I bade him good night, he really appeared to be a very wiselike, weel-doing man.

In the course of the night, however, or rather towards the morning, I was molested with a great ringing of bells; and, by and by, a waiter looked in on me, and cried that Mr Roslin was on the floor, in the jaws of death; bidding me get up and come, which I was not long of doing; and there was he lying in an apoplexy, with the complexion of a bandana pocket-napkin. Was not that very extraordinary?

But, not to summer and winter on the catastrophe, the long and the short of it was that he departed this life in a short time – less than an hour; and I was left with the dead body on my hands, not knowing what to do with it, being demented with consternation. Before, however, I proceed to relate the terrible things which ensued, it behoves me to make a few words of improvement on what had come to pass; for as much will, no doubt, be expected from a person like me, whose duty it is, by his vocation, to turn the calamities of life to a profit.

First, then, it cannot be denied that Mr Roslin dying suddenly in the hands of strangers, was an event to make an impression on the hearts of professing Christians; and,

Second, That his leaving, on so slight an acquaintanceship, a sum of money to me, to buy a mourning ring, was a most uncommon thing; for the which there was, no doubt, a purpose, though he was taken away before that purpose was revealed.

The uncertainty of life was visible in his death; and the wonders that come upon us like seeming chances, kythed in the provisions of his will; of which I will have to be more particular when I describe what happened after his interment. But it was a stang in the vitals to think how I, a quiet country minister, dwelling in the peacefulness of my manse, should have been innocently drawn into such a slough of despond; and shews, in a most edifying manner, that we know not what a day may bring forth.

Chapter XVI

After the breath of life was out of the body, and the folk of the inn had, in a most creditable manner – they could not have done better in a manse – got the remains straighted, I went again to my bed, fashed with what had come to pass, and soon after fell into a dover, that slippit into a sleep. In the morning, being awoke, I rose, and all the time I was eating my breakfast, had disconsolate thoughts; for I pondered how I was to get the dead buried; because he dying in an inn, which is a public, assoilyied the magistrates from the obligation of granting me an indemnification for the cost; and where was the justice of taxing me for the interment of a stranger? To let a dead corpse lie in the house for ever, it was not reasonable to expect the landlord would allow: – who then was to be at the expense of the removal?

Then I considered well that a lair was to be had – who was to be at the outlay for one? – for it was well known that Sir Michael made the toun council pay for the burying ground; and how could they be reimbursed, if every grave was to be free gratis? – besides, who was to pay the betherel for howking it? In short, the more I reflected on the bearings of the case – as an elder, who was an advocate, in the General Assembly, said – I was the more constipated; but out of my perplexities I got, in a sense, by the landlord coming into the room.

'Sir,' said he, 'this is a sad affair; for I understand from the waiter that the dead gentleman, was, in a manner, an utter stranger to you, and that you had some reason to suspect he was left by the Yankee vessel in straitened circumstances. What is to be done?'

'That is just what I think – what *is* to be done?'

'Has he no friends?'

'He left the east country many years ago, a perfect orphan, and he found the land of his birth a desolation.'

'Very bad! I wish he had not died in my house. Had he no friend but you?'

'It could not be lawfully said that I am sib to him, either as kith or kin.'

'Well, but who else was he known to?'

'I fear that your trust is a broken reed: he came to me with Mr Ettles, who, more than a dozen of years ago was a merchant, and perished the pack with his uncle.'

I made this answer, for I was terrified for a responsibility, and thought it best to be guarded.

'I see how it is,' answered the landlord. 'I must, in the first instance, risk the outlay; but do me the favour to superintend the funeral, to see that no unnecessary expense is incurred; and write to Mr Ettles concerning what has happened.'

This I agreed to; and, in the course of the day, I was visited by several gospel-hearted persons, who condoled with me. The ministers of the town make it a point never to visit strangers in affliction; for, in a sea-port, that might be very troublesome.

Then, with the advice of the landlord, I set about the funeral, which I was for having with more frugality than him; but he said Mr Roslin came to his house and lived in it like a gentleman, and he could not be answerable to himself or the world if he sent him out of it as anything less; so we had a most decent ploy – everything creditable and no waste.

By the time, on the day of the burial, that we came back from the new kirkyard – as the Greenock folk call their burying-ground, though there was then no kirk near it, but only a Relief hobbleshow – there came a letter from London, directed for Mr Roslin; which the landlord, contrary to my solid advice, opened in presence of witnesses. However, this letter was from Mr Ettles, saying, he had invested the money agreeably to orders, and wishing him a pleasant meeting with all their friends in the other world; which, to hear, made my very heart loup to my lips – it was so like blasphemy; for Mr Roslin was but minded to go to America, and had no thoughts of another world, though making his will. The landlord said, however, that there was a day-break in the letter, which I did not well see, and took upon himself to correspond with Mr Ettles; but added – 'Before I write, there is a desk which must be examined, that I may tell what is in it.'

Accordingly, we had the desk brought down by a waiter lad, and found a key that opened it in the pocket of the waistcoat that the deceased had worn on the day before his departal. But what was in the desk need not be rehearsed – only there was found in it a will which he had penned after I had left him; and we all held up our hands in wonderment at it; concerning the cause of which, I will relate in the next chapter.

Chapter XVII

The last will and testament of Mr Roslin was a very well-penned manuscript paper. No lawyer's instrument could have been more to the purpose; for it testified that he was a man of substance, and could very well afford all the legacies it set forth – the chief of which was five thousand dollars to me, because I was a worthy character, overflowing with simplicity and truth.

This was the only alteration made to the will by which he left the hundred dollars to buy the ring, and I would have been most unreasonable to have objected to the alteration. The residue of his fortune he left to Mr Ettles; who, in short, when all was done, was a well-pleased inheritor to a nest egg that was not addled. But many things must, *à priori*, be rehearsed.

Thus, it came to pass, on the day after the interment, that I deemed it expedient to return to the manse and to my sister, who I thought could not be an easy woman because of my absence, she only knowing for cause that I was detained by Mr Roslin, who had gone off in an apoplexy. But before I left the Tontine Inn, I wrote a particular letter to Mr Ettles, advising him to come (meaning, if he could afford it, for I remembered he had been a broken merchant) and see after the will and the residue; telling him how discreet the landlord had been, and how abstemious the ministers were obligated to be, by a sense of duty, as to giving consolation to strangers respecting whom they knew nothing.

When the porter of the inn, a Celt, said, comically enough, that he had post-poned my letter, I took my stick in my hand and leisurely walked away to the ferry. The day, when I did so, was not bright, as was reasonable to be expected in a place of the well-known habitudes of Greenock; but it was dry then; and, accordingly, as I went along by myself, I had time for reflection. I had not, however, gone far, when the wind began to spit in my face; and, before I got to the end of my journey, me and a wet man were none different. Indeed, I could not go into the boat by reason of my wetness, and was obligated to bide in the ferry-house till my clothes were dried, putting on a petticoat-commodity of the landlady's till my own nether vestment was dried on a chair-back afore the fire.

At last, I was ready for the road, and, stepping into the ferry boat, got safe over, and in due season arrived at the manse; where that very attentive creature, sister Becky, had the kettle boiling, and made me as comfortable as could well be, considering.

When I had taken a dish of tea, which was very refreshing, I told my sister all that had come to pass; and more especially about the ring and the legacy. But she was clearly of opinion that I ought to have nothing to do with either, knowing so little as we did of Mr Roslin, who certainly could have no good intent in making what seemed a benison, in dollars, instead of pounds sterling – for a most uncertain coin is dollars. It was evidently a castle in the air, luring into a lawsuit.

My fears did not carry me so far as my sister's scrupulosities did her;

but, nevertheless, a fyke fell upon me, and I wearied exceedingly for a response from Mr Ettles, walking much by myself, and meditating on the nothingness of this world.

At last, a letter came, of which I could make neither heads nor tails, farther than that Mr Ettles would soon be with me, and that Mr Roslin was reputed to be a rich man; giving me no reason, however, to think how, as my sister said, he could, by a possibility, leave me a legacy, which, if the dollar was no more than four-and-tenpence, as she had known it to be, would still be a happy godsend. Altogether, it is not to be told what we suffered at this time; for Becky, to increase my tribulations, had glimpses of visions and trances, wherein she thought she saw that I was doomed to receive a true legacy, and conjectured about buying many needful articles for the manse that we had never wanted till 'the gowden brae seemed to shoot on us.'

Seeing her, who was upon the whole a wise-like woman, falling into inordinate fits, I communed with myself, and resolved, until Mr Ettles came, to make no change in my own walk and conversation. Accordingly, I made a point of preaching, not a new sermon, but one that was well thumbed; and I baptized two children on the next Sabbath, as composedly as if nothing had come to pass. But, for all that I did not repose on a bed of roses, as may well be supposed by those who have experienced similar vicissitudes. At last, we heard Mr Ettles was coming down to settle everything, and begging me to meet him at Edinburgh; which was far from my hand to do, for I really had no faith in the legacy, nor could I say that my sister had oftentimes brighter expectations, especially when she talked with a rational sobriety. However, from less to more, I was in the end persuaded to go to the tryst, whereof I have now to relate the particulars.

Chapter XVIII

To the 'Guid Toun,' it may be inferred from what is set forth in the foregoing chapter, I did go, and by the fly from Greenock to Glasgow, and thence to Edinburgh, all in one day; and who was at the coach door, but Mr Ettles, who was most extraordinary glad to see me?

After the usual *parley vous*, he took me to the inns where he himself was staying; and, as I had come well on to seventy miles that day, a scomfished man I surely was, in great need of a cordial drink of tea, which I soon had; and being greatly recruited by the same, we spent a very instructive evening.

From him I learned that Mr Roslin was a man who died in a well-doing circumstance – who having no near kindred that he knew of, had long intimated his intention of leaving Mr Ettles his heir, not jalousing, however, that he was so nigh unto his own latter end as this come-to-pass had made manifest. In short, when he told me of many ins and outs, I wrote my sister about it, in a line by the next post, to let her know that I had gotten well to Edinburgh, without an accident, and that there was a prospect, through Mr Ettles, that the legacy would be something more of a substantiality than the wind of the mouth.

In the morning after, Mr Ettles could not but see I was fashed; and inquired, in a most sympathizing manner, anent the occasion, which caused me to say to him that it was a certain loss to come into Edinburgh, if all I had for it was the prospect of him going over the sea, as he had told me, the bulk of Mr Roslin's gathering being there.

At first he gave me a sudden glower; but soon after, he relapsed into his ordinary, and said, to give myself no concern about him; adding, it was, at most, but a trip across the Atlantic, which he thought nothing of.

This, no doubt, was an ease of mind, especially when he mentioned that it was his intention to pay off all the legacies first and foremost, as plenty assets to do so were in this country; and then he could take his own will with the residue, he being, in the words of the king's law, residuary legatee.

Still, in all this, I could not discern for what he wanted me in Edinburgh, and so I asked him, even down, the reason; which he laughingly said was to see how I would comport myself under my good fortune – a very unsatisfactory answer, for not a preeing of good fortune had I yet gotten; and, notwithstanding all that he had told me, I could not but feel I had only a cold coal to blow at; and that the outlay on the incoming was sure, and no trifle. But, as no better could then be made o't, I submitted myself to a gospel resignation, resolving not to kick against the pricks.

By and by, however, it came out that he was a more searching man than I had supposed; for he had learnt that some needcessitous relations of Mr Roslin were about the closes of the Canongate; and he was minded, if he could find them out, to make a division among them, and had thought that I might be of use in assisting him in that Christian quest. This I was well pleased to hear, for it was just like him to do so, as I ever thought by what I had seen from the first when he came to the manse a wooer of Miss Silvia Graham, of whom I have made mention, and who certainly was the loveliest creature that ever my eyes set on. His second wife was but a coarse worsted commodity compared to yon silken negligee. But, before I rehearse the upshot of our inquisition of the closes and unsavoury nooks of the Cowgate, as well as all the Canongate, it is necessary to say something of the town of Edinburgh, which, among the best-informed of the inhabitants, has not its marrow on this side of the New Jerusalem, that is paved with precious stones.

Chapter XIX

From auld lang syne, I had made it a rule to make observes in every foreign place I went to, after I was placed; which accounts for the insight of the world in these pages. It is not, therefore, to be thought that I would go about in such a town as Edinburgh surely is, with my eyes shut; and so, the better to enlighten the reader as to what I have to tell, it behoves me firstly to make it plain what my notion is in general of our old Scottish capital, wherein the Court of Session and the General Assembly are still allowed, by the prelatic Parliament of England, to hold their sederunts.

Now, I mean to be as plain as I am pleasant; for there are things in which diffidence is no virtue; and if I should make some folks claw where it's no youky, the fault is not in me, but in their own position. First and verily, I do aver, without the possibility of a denial, that Edinburgh, to say no ill of it, is one of the most self-conceited Babels that ever the Lord put the breath of life into; and certain it is, among the residenters, there are some who would give more for a forebear in a stoury lead kist than for a living preacher of the gospel. But no to be overly salt upon them, I ought to make a Nota Bene, that maybe they are not utterly void of kindness – of the which, me and Mr Ettles had a large experience among his acquaintance; for what with them that had new silver plate work to shew, and others that were sleeping partners, no doubt, in wine concerns, and had many sample bottles to pree, we had, as I heard a Paddy's man on the top of the fly say, 'a galoring of dinnering.' But there is much new-fangled bravery yonder; and sure am I, for all their sprose, that a silver tea-pot of the godly days of John Knox and the Lords of the Congregation, is not to be found within the four walls of the place.

One thing bred me much consternation – for it was never well cleared up – and that was a notion I had gotten somehow at the Divinity Hall of Glasgow, that there were only swans to be seen among the poultry of Edinburgh. I can, however, safely affirm on my conscience that I never saw a swan there. Only very common gooses are to be met with at the best tables; and it's my sedate opinion, that not one of their Ordinary Lords would ken, in a sense, a goose from a swan, though he saw it gabbling on the floor of the Parliament House.

I am the more particular anent this, because I was nearly shot through the lights and vitals, by a look that a leddy threw at me when she asked me to be helped one day to a calf's head. 'Na,' quo' I, 'that, madam, is no dainties; but I'll take a slice from the bosom of yon swan that's afore your guidman.' 'A swan!' quo' she. 'Ay, a swan,' quo' I – 'isna all the Edinburgh gooses swans?' The which response raised a mighty shout of laughter; but I saw, with the tail of my eye, that some of the professors and other literary characters then present, were near hand guffawing with the wrong sides of their mouths. Oh, yon are comical folk! Gude keep me from their gooses' and calfs' heads!

Upon the whole, I'll no undertake to maintain that 'Auld Reeky' is just the land of Canaan. It may be, however, no a desolation to them that can fen on their own pock nook; but they maun ca' canny; for the acting yonder's no in a way of moderation. Their wedding-like banquets are a sign that they are sometimes obligated to sup muslin kail as a consequence, as well as handle the drumsticks of poney cocks for a fortnight after.

But though this is in a manner holy writ, concerning the general carnality of the place, yet it's no a town without garnels of the Lord in by places, as I will have occasion to shew and testify when I come to set down many things of which me and Mr Ettles had a verification to our senses, when we came to explorify the closes. Indeed, my chief purpose in speaking of the upping of the garnish inhabitants was, that the courteous reader might discern how it happens that a portion of the decent people shrink into closes, and scogs in wynds. – It is because they cannot vie with those that are no better than themselves; for, having a right notion of Christianity, they do not put out their arms farther than their sleeves will let; which, in the vernacular, signifies, they live within their incomes. In short, I could see that a lord's living would not play pue to an Edinburgh writer, buying land with a wadset; and it belongs to me, seeing so much of the world as I have seen, by being at the head of a parish, to testify my displeasure against all sorts of the prevailing immortality.

Chapter XX

It becomes a man whose duty it is to shew how the hardships of this life may be softened to the sense, to make himself acquainted with the dens of depravity and the hiding-places of wo; for, although it would not be right nor just to say that crime and poverty are either sib or connected, it is well known that they are near neighbours: and me and Mr Ettles saw this, in our visitations to the purlieus of the Canongate and the Cowgate. There the thief and the beggar dwell in the same close; and ne'er-do-weel cutties in garret-rooms up dark unwashen turnpike stairs, where many a godly weanless widow is constrained, by the unaccountable dispensations of mercy, to read her Bible in solitude, and make her meal of resignation.

Considering the intent of his quest, and the weight that curiosity had with myself, to see the haunts of want and iniquity, that I might edify my own people with a true account of them when I returned home; I said to Mr Ettles that I would, if he were willing, much rather enter on our business at once, than go to any more dinners with corky-headed advocates; for really they did not agree with me, and were of a nature, by reason of the aloes and myrrh wherewith they were in a sense served, to make the plain fare of the manse seem wersh and unsavoury.

He agreed with me that they certainly had such a tendency, and likewise that we should not delay our search; but when I thought, afterwards, how a paid porter might have explorified as well as us, I was troubled in mind to think if he could be actuated by a wish to find Mr Roslin's cousin, or to see the ferlies which are in the dark and secret abysses of the lower orders. 'Deed, I need not disguise it, as it did seem sometimes to me, by what fell from him, that he was moved more by a wish to see how I would comport myself in the howffs of squalor, than to find either kith or kin of Mr Roslin's; for he often said that the innocence and peace of a country parish made it a garden of Eden, compared to this world of a metropolis. But, although I may not penetrate into the mysteries of his thoughts, they are nevertheless patent to One who will judge of them aright; not that I think it could be a real deadly sin to dive with inquisitive eyes into the subterranean regions of Edinburgh, which the wynds and closes are, and yon dreadful darksome stairs, the broken windows whereof are mended in a way, with old hats and the cast cla'es of beggary.

Having wrought Mr Ettles into a Christian frame, to go in search of Mr Roslin's cousin, that might be discovered needful of a legacy, somewhere adjacent to the Parliament House, we fixed on the morn's morning after, to set out together; but, although at first he seemed very instantaneous to go, yet I could discern in the end a growing reluctance, as if he jaloused no cousin was there to be found; and I said to him that, should it so be, we would nevertheless see those things which are not shewn to kings and the princes of the earth, and which give a value to the mercies that the greatest possess; an exhortation which incited him to come with me. In his compliance, however, I had my own think; for he it was that first clockit the project, and why he came afterwards to fall into the dubieties about it, was a wonder, needing interpretation. Altogether, though riper intimacy made me notice many things in Mr Ettles to knit him closer and closer to my regards, there began to kithe about him something which I did not well understand; and now and then I could see, or thought I saw, a predominance of superiority, as if I stood before him as in the presence of one that had a discerning spirit, and was loath to give it head-rope. This was the more mystical, as I was surely fully his equal; being a minister of the gospel, placed in a parish with a sufficiency of stipend; and he, to say the least of it, only a damaged mercantile, with the prospect of a legacy from an unco. But I am transgressing on what should not yet be told, until I have given a particular account of what befel us in the unclean receptacles and odoriferous nooks of Edinburgh.

Chapter XXI

Alas, when I think on what we saw in yon caverns of sorrow, never more can I doubt, even in the finest day, that this is not a world of sin and misery.

Our first pilgrimage was along Princes' Street, and across the North Bridge; and, at the corner where it enters the High Street we halted, looking about us to discover where we should begin. Then Mr Ettles suggested that we ought to go up the Castle Hill, and come down, close by close, so as to leave not one without an investigation, till we had reached the sanctified kennel of the Abbey. I thought so too; for, since we were on a search of discovery, we could not be too particular. Accordingly, we went towards the king's stronghold, and I have now to relate our adventures and observes.

The first place we went into was of a declivity nature, in a land of houses, with an outside stair, near the Castle Hill. It was not remarkable, and the inhabitants, chiefly of the female gender in a state of widowhood, were elderly and composed persons, all looking from their doors and windows at the sight of a minister, and a gentleman likewise in black, asking for one Archibald Junor; for it was a cousin by the mother's side that we were in quest of; which causes me to make mention that I think folk are naturally more addicted to their mother's friends than their father's; which is mystical, for, by rights of nature, fathers are nearer than mothers, No doubt, however, this is one of the blemishes to which the children of Adam became liable by the fall.

In that close, we could hear nothing, and we came away to the next; remarking that closes on the skirts of towns are more cleanly than those sinks of iniquity that are in the throng places, types of the sinfulness that is foul at the heart of man.

Then we entered another, a long entry leading to a place that led downwards; and I doubt if there innocence was thriving, for it was very dirty, and the ragged callans and bardy lassies were not overly civilized, nor their parents, I suspect, of the elect. There, too, our pains were abortive; only a fat woman, more indeed, for manners, like a trumpeter of dragoons than the wife of a douce man, gave me a slap on the shoulder, and nicheringly inquired if I wanted to spy the nakedness of the land; at the which Mr Ettles looked at her pawkily.

We then soberly daunered into a third refuge of the destitute. Like its predecessor, but something more, it abounded in slovenly-dressed women, who might be single; some of them, I thought, might have had other tow to spin that to be standing with the keys of their garret-rooms in their hands, hearing and telling new things. When I saw these Edinburgh calamities, I thought of the Athenians.

But this close was not the wilderness of Marah; for, as we were coming away genty, a donsy creature said, with something like Christianity in her voice –

'Maybe ye're seeking for the poor man that's bed-fast aboon. I'll shew you his lodging; for he cannot be out of the need of an awmous.'

We followed her, and she led us up a dark timber stair, and shewed us into a chamber that was no better than a wastage. There, on the floor, on a pickle straw, beneath the residue of an old carpet, lay a lamiter man, wearying, as he said, for death.

My heart filled full at the sight; and Mr Ettles gave the Mary Magdalene who guided us up, something out of his waistcoat pocket, saying to me, 'The precious stone is bright on the dunghill.'

'What are ye, honest man?' quo' I to the invalid; which caused him to look at me with the glittering eye of one in a sore fever; and drawing the bit rag over his head, as if to eschew our sight, he responded, with a sad sullenness –

'A man.'

'So I see,' was my compassionate answer; 'but tell us what ye were?'

'A beggar, as long as I could; now illness has made me bankrupt – a bankrupt beggar – for I cannot stir from the pallet of starvation.'

His words bespoke breeding; and I turned, in a very tender-hearted mood to Mr Ettles, and inquired what he thought: to which he replied – 'He must be the Archibald Junor we are in search of;' and looked at me with a sorrowful countenance; whereupon, the true nature of our errand to those uncomely places came, like the element of light into the darkness, on my simple ignorance; and I said, 'No possible!'

The damsel was still standing by; and while we were thus speaking, she bended down and churmed something into the lug of the dying man. What he said to her we did not hear; but, as she raised herself, he drew his hap closer over him.

'For godsake, gentlemen,' then said she, 'first gie him help, and then talk.'

I trow Mr Ettles did not need another instigation; he cried to her to run for a doctor, and to fetch cordials, giving her wherewithal to buy what was wanted. I must, however, reserve what ensued for another chapter.

Chapter XXII

The pitiful damsel vanished outright, as if the very rowels of the spur of charity were up to their heads in the side of her heart; and we were left with the man, that, till we came, had been helpless, not knowing what to say or do, but afflicted with a palsy of consternation.

When we had stood some time, looking down at him on the straw on the floor, he pulled the bit dirty carpet off his face, and casting up towards us the pale eyes of a passer from the world, requested me to give him a drink of water, which I saw in a porringer on the floor. In the room was neither seat nor table; but, to be sure, I was not long of handing and helping him to what he asked.

He drank as one that was very dry; but before I took the porringer from his lips, there was a visible alteration in his countenance, and in his throat a sound.

Me and Mr Ettles were both awed and silent; for the king of terrors was then plainly busy making a conquest. Presently after, drawing a long sigh, the summoned departed, and his mortal remains lay before us, stiffening and still – a lean morsel for the insatiable grave.

There was a fearful haste, as it were, in this come to pass, that took away any small presence of mind I possessed; and Mr Ettles cried, 'Good God!'

Then we heard a foot coming up the dark timber stair, and angrily muttering, 'Damnation ' the which word, to hear at that time, struck me as a blasphemy or a doom. But I had not long to ruminate; for in came the doctor that the lass had sent, who, in coming up the stair, had met with a difficulty.

He was a young man, smelling of lavender water; and he looked about the room, when he entered, as if the air of it was unsavoury. Then he gave a glance at the mort, and said, 'The man is dead – it was of no use to send for me.'

Hearing him so hale-hearted, and seeing the dejection of Mr Ettles, I felt my corruption rise; but, before I could put a few words of smeddum together, he walked away, and left us standing in postures of grief.

Not long after, the ministering maiden returned, with a black choppin bottle, without a cork, in her hand; and falling on her knees beside the corpse, she lifted the porringer, which I had been using, and poured into it from the bottle as much as a glass of whisky, which she held to the lips of that which had been man.

'It's too late, my leddy,' said I – 'he's done now with the bitters and the sweets of this life.'

Whereupon she rose from her kneeling; and Mr Ettles bidding her get what was necessary done, and he would pay for it, took me by the arm, and led me, without speaking, down into the Lawnmarket, where he said –

'This is more than I had bargained for; but the scene could not be uncommon, for many mendicants are in the world, and some of them must daily die.'

He then fell into a reverie, and as we walked back to the inns, was evidently, as might be expected, inwardly troubled. As for me, I was filled with thankfulness and resignation for my lot having been cast in a lown manse, afar from the spectacles wherewith a sinful world abounds.

In the course of the afternoon, he thawed into more composity, and said, sedately, that he feared I had much reason to be displeased with him; telling me that, by the friendship of Mr Roslin, finding himself much farther aboon the world than he ever expected to be, and the whole scheme of his being again changed, he had thought he might, by my means, gain an insight that would, at least to himself, be edifying; for, said he –

'Though I have met with many possessed of great knowledge of the world – of that knowledge by which men know how they may swindle with respectability – I never saw a man like you, who so unconsciously read the heart, and yet practised so little or had so little of that suspicion which is the basis of the world's craft. But what we have seen to-day has changed my purpose; I will pay you at once the legacy, and lead you no more to such sights of distress; for, verily, it cannot be wise to look at the sad side of things.'

There was something in this that caused me to ponder; but still I could not away with what we had witnessed, and I thought the legacy a heavy handful, for exposing me to such trials as we had come through that day, especially the upshot.

Chapter XXIII

Oh, humanity! frail, ever-erring, inconsistent thing! But first let me tell what happened; for maybe the bare recital of it will, of itself, be a sufficient morality.

In the evening, after drinking our tea, being very dolorous and down-hearted about the worldly condition of sinful man, and communing of the awful sight me and Mr Ettles had seen in the forenoon, we were sitting in the inns – no singing, I am sure, the spring of 'O'er the bogie' – when the waiter lad came in, with a jokefellow-like smirk, and said to me, that two ladies were in the street, wishing a word o' me; and, turning round, he added, to Mr Ettles, in a hauflin whisper, but loud enough for me to hear, that he durst not bring them into the house.

Mr Ettles *instanter* rose and left his seat and the room, leaving me all alone with the waiter, who did not seem to be too douce. But I inquired of him wherefore the leddies that wanted me durst not come into the house, saying – 'For, no doubt, if they wanted a word in secret, it would be more decent in-doors than out in the thoroughfare.'

'So it would,' replied he, with a havrel chuckle; adding that, as I was a minister, maybe, if I spoke to the master, he would let me bring them in.

Mr Ettles having gone away, I then sent the lad to ask the landlord; jalousing that his house, for an inns, being a sober sojourn, and the leddies maybe a wee quiscoskos in character, might be the reason of the prohibition. I told him also what a gask we had met with, that he might inform the master it was to a moral certainty the leddies had come about the dead man.

The news were as a miracle wrought upon the publican and sinner; for the landlord not only consented to let the leddies come in to me, but the poor lad, with his libertine nicher, was converted into as awful a thing as an elder at the brod, in the eyes of a wean that lays its first bawbee in the plate; which, by the by, in our kirk does not often happen, for the parish is in the country, and we only make a collection at the Occasion. But to proceed.

As I was going to say, the waiter had not been long on his errand, till back he came, shewing in the two scuffed women.

One of them was she that had played the part of Mary Magdalene, with the bottle and the porringer, as I have rehearsed; the other demosle – for I can call her nothing else – seemed to be a new recruit to the clanjamphry.

They had both glistening eyes and bleezy faces. I had my doubts – gude forgie me if I blaspheme her good name! – that the strange woman was the waur of liquor; for, when she sat down on a chair, she swayed hither and yon, and was so coggly that I had my fears of a catastrophe on the floor.

When they had been some time sederunt, the one I had foregathered with in the house of mourning said that she had been advised by her friend, Miss Gills, there, to let me know that all was sorted, and she was sure, to my liking; and to invite me up at the guessing time of the gloaming, to see that she did not dankle the truth.

'We have gotten a coffin from the session.' said she, 'and Mrs Farls has spoken for the shortbread to Mr Daigh, the baxter; only, as the outlay has been great, we'll need a replenishment to buy the wine, which, Miss Gills thinks, considering how you were present at the dead-ill, cannot, in Christianity, be dispensed with; for you know the ministers of the city will, no doubt, be invited by you to partake of the burial. As for the ministers, however, I'm not for them; for they are prideful creatures; and, if they gaed to beggars' late-wakes, they might not have time to make sermons for the gentlefolks.'

I cannot but say that I was dumbfoundered so to hear her speak, and would have been at a loss what to say, had not Miss Gills, at that very moment, given a great hiccup, and no being in an elbow chair, coupit off with a circumbendibus, which caused me – no used to pull bells – to give a great alarm, that brought in the landlord, Mr Ettles, and the waiter, who all had surely been just at the door when the fracas happened.

Chapter XXIV

It is not to be told what ensued from Miss Gills' accident; but the upshot was that the poor donsy leddies were sent away with a flea in their lug. I could, not, however, approve of the way the waiter conducted himself towards them; for he was desperate venomous, and ranted at them as if they had been tinselers, and he himself one of a moral principle. As for Mr Ettles, he said nothing, but looked pitiful, and the landlord sympathized with what I suffered; for, oh, yon was a humbling sight! far waur to the eye of the spirit than the starvation of the beggar man, in which the hand of a just Lord was visibly laid on for sins and iniquities he had seen; but with the poor outcasts, there was only a kithing of the original guilt of our fallen nature. So, although I might have been righteously very angry at them, I was sorrowful unto a sickness of the heart, and soon after retired to my room, to have an investigation of my own unworthiness.

At supper-time, when I came down stairs, I found Mr Ettles sitting by himself in a pondering posture; and he said –

'It is too late now for me to experiment with characters. The friendship of Mr Roslin renewed for a time, as it were, my youth, and I fancied that I might revive old tastes and predilections; but years and vicissitudes have wrought a change, of which till this day I was insensible.'

He then looked at me with a concerned eye, and, after a space, subjoined –

'I am sure you will pardon me: – I but thought the poor entitled to a portion of the legacy left me, and had recourse to the stratagem which I practised with you to see their dwellings. There was no such person as that Junor whom we went in quest of; and I ask your pardon for having made you see sights that must have scalded with anguish your heart. But the last remaining dream of youth is now over; and the remainder of a life that has not been all sunshine, shall be spent in the usages of other men.'

Upon reflection, I was not content to think he had invited me to visit yon abominable corners of Edinburgh, because maybe he thought I could afford it out of the legacy which he had wised in a sense to me; but there was about him, at that time, a something which fell heavy upon me, even like sadness; for really Mr Ettles had from the first seemed a man by ordinar: though making his bread by merchandizing, he was, as I would say, created and born for to be a philosopher. I never saw his marrow, nor one who had his will in such subjection to his own management. Not, however, to summer and winter more about him, I have only to mention that, next day, he paid me to the utmost farthing my bequest, and while I returned to the manse, made the best of his way to London.

Thus concluded that sore thing which occasioned me to indite this writing; and Becky, my sister, had no cause to be ill-pleased at the upshot, though sometimes a woman no overly content with the dispensations of Providence. Mr Ettles bought and sent to her by me a most grand silver tea-pot; having heard her once say that a manse with such a utensil was a match for a Highland gentleman's tappytourock dwelling.

A RICH MAN; OR, HE HAS GREAT MERIT

BEING THE
AUTOBIOGRAPHY OF ARCHIBALD PLACK, ESQ.,
LATE LORD MAYOR OF LONDON,
IN A SERIES OF LETTERS TO HIS GRANDSON,
THE HONOURABLE GEORGE SPEND

Letter I

My oe and heir, ye kenna-what, how can ye think that ganging a grey gaet is the way to turn the penny, unless it be out of your pouch? It wasna, my lad, by such gavalling that I gart the bodles whelp in mine; and, therefore, instead of sending you 'a replenishment' at this time, I'll send you much better, being an account of the different come-to-passes in my creditable life. They'll maybe serve you as well as Latin books, which are only things that may do good to doctors, and others that follow the poor trade of philosophy; which, with God's help and my bit haining, I hope you are never ordained to take up: no that I make an objek to birkies of a pedigree – as surely you are, by the father's side – to get a slaik of college lair; but it's no to be feart that ye'll ever be dour at your books.

It's very true that my Lord, your father, that's married upon my only dochter, your mother, is a discreet man – and there was a good because he should be so; for the auld Lord, his father, was a canary-headed sorrow, and didna leave a crumb or moulin of his patrimony out of the coomy clutches of the lawyers and Jews; so that, had he no forgatherit with your mother, my dochter, he would just, in a sense, have been going from door to door, with a meal pock about his neck, and a rung in his hand – no living at heck and manger, as he is now doing, in yon Castle Folly, in Vanity Fair, as the west end of the town ought by rights to be called.

But, before I get all the rift off my stomach, it is needful to remark, that, although I dinna intend to be as mim as a May puddock with you, yet I'm no of an overly virgos nature, even in my displeasure about your galravitching and keeping of an eating horse; on the contrary, I'm of a most natural mild temper, as in the end you may experience: indeed, if I'm no so to my only dochter's kitling, I wonder to wha I should be so. But what I have to say is all for your good; and I redd you no to take it ill, for I have my will and testament to make; and all I have is of my own conkesting, which frees me from leaving a doit to your father's get, unless it pleasure myself; and yet there is not a living Christian that better kens that blood is thicker than water than I do. And, Geordie, although ye were not a Lord's offspring, I cannot but recognise you as my only daughter's affset – my bark is mair dauntoning than my bite.

I dinna mind if ever I told you anent my ancestors; and I am sure my dochter Climy, your mother, never would, for she was aye an upsetting cutty; it therefore behoves me to let you know whatna brae I have had to climb, that ye may see riches are no gatherit like sclate stanes, to the end that ye may consider well of writing to me letters anent replenishments, keeping, as I am creditably informed you do, an eating moth of a horse of the hunter speshy – maybe two, one for a flunkie. Geordie, Geordie, ca' canny! Hunters and racers are genteel creatures; and I would have as meikle hope of a ne'er-do-weel with a laithron, as a young man with such gambolling cattle: the very whisk of their tails is an evendown outrage among decent folk. From this you may learn what is in my breast concerning this wastry; and, by the next post, I'll make a beginning, which is all at present from your auld daddy,

Archd. Plack

Letter II

Although is is not to be looked for in the course of nature that a man can have a very clear recollection of the hour he was born; yet he is seldom long in the world till he learns whether he is cast into the lot of Dives or of Lazarus. For my part, I was not left to consider which was mine; for, ever since I could tell a cold chucky-stone from a laughing het potato, I have had a notion that man is the heir of afflictions; accordingly, I felt it soon to by my duty to ettle what I could to get into a way. And that I soon did; for, being a gair and stirring laddie wean, folk took notice of me, and mony a bawbee I got by my glegness in running errands; less thoughtful callans would have waur'd on marbles, or played at the unthrift of pitch-and-toss, but I had a natural appety all my days for saving, and told mother to put my bawbees in a tea-cup, for she was obligated in course of nature to keep me till I came to years of discretion.

My mother was a pawkie carlin – I mind her weel; and she said, when I spoke of haining, that I was no ordained to be long a cess on her; for my speech kythed wi' symptoms that discretion was not far off when I was near – and so it was seen; for, when I was scrimp six, her dead-ill fell upon her, and, being a sailor's widow, she departed this life, leaving me an orphan to an old aunty with few teeth and of a cankry inclination; having but her spinning-wheel for her bread-winner.

However, aunty did her duty; and, as I had nine pence halfpenny when I went to domicile with her, she sent me to the school; for which every week I paid a penny, and every day read in the Mother's Carritches; so that, before I had won through the Sixpence, I was accounted, by her and the minister's leddy, a deacon of a scholar. The minster himself patted my head because of my profishency.

But, although it couldna but be said that I learnt to read like a bailie in the course of the first winter I was at the school, yet there was an outcoming of fortune in the spring that detained me from learning any more till the next winter; and this was the coming into the clachan of a soldier officer with a timber leg and a fashious temper, who needed a gleg callan to do his turns.

By dint of speaking well of me, aunty, through the minister, got Captain Sash to give me a preferment; but I had a sore time o't in attending to his yeas and nays, specially in the warm months, when flies are bloody-minded, and, as he often said, most damnable.

How long I might have bided in the servitude of Captain Sash is not to be rehearsed; but, towards the hinder end of har'st, we parted; and the chief because of the amputation was his wooden leg, with which he was in the scowry nights, by habit and repute, in the way of riping the ribs. Thus it came to pass, that he came home one evening, and the fire being low, and he being cauldrife, lifted his timber toe and gave it a powter.

Gude kens how it came to pass, but in so doing he staggers, his wooden leg was among hands broken, and he wytes me with the exploit; which I would not thole, for it was not true; whereat he called me a mutinous vagabond. My corruption rose. I replied he was a scarlet tyrant; he lifted his hand, I jouked the blow, and he, having but one leg to stand on, swung round and fell on the coals, which it was a mercy were not kindled. He paid me, howsever, my wage; for, though of a frush temper, he had a modicum of honesty about him. Nothing, however, would persuade me to come again within his reach; for even then I was a spirit.

With the wage, aunty put me again to school, to learn to write and cast 'counts, for I had learnt, as I have told you, to read; but in this political economy I was not cordial; for, understanding that the session was obligated to do something for me, I was loath to part with my penny-fee, for no other end, that I could see at the time, than to draw crunkly effigies on paper and a sclate. But I soon came to discern the good that was in them; and, before Candlemas, the dominie said I was a geni – telling aunty, though, it was kittle to say for what. I think myself it was a geni for making money, as, before the Candlemas, I had hained, from going errands, two shillings and five and a bawbee; and when the thought came into my head, that my capacity was of the peinor-pig order, it is not to be told what a revelation I had. I was, in sooth, a pawkie wean, and kent a mite by its mudging from a moulin.

But of that blithe and heartsome time – it may be of scant and want – I have not much remembrance. Like others, I have a pleasant recollection of my ramplar days. The summer was warmer then, and surely winter brisker. Oh, the pretty moonlights! Surely Time has grown aulder, and a thought tavert since syne; and I think Nature now is wersher of the smeddum than that she then sowed into the young heart. But I was never one that neglectit a turn for daffin.

Letter III

When I had perfited my edication, which was afore Beltane of the next year – I being then weel through my eighth year – it behoved me to think of some gaet of going to the the world to seek a living; for it was not thought I was of a proper habit of body for a trade, as I was short-sighted, and very ready to take the cold, which shewed that herding would never do for me. Some calling of a sheltered nature was, therefore, to be thought of. The neighbours of aunty considered, however, I was still young enough; but there was a confabble among them anent me, which made it manifest that there would soon be an outcoming.

In the May after, the laddie who kirned James Junor's, the druggist, medicaments, took the kingcost; and, being of a weakly constitution, paid the debt of nature in no time. Thus there came to be a vacuity in the druggist's shop, and I was elected, by James, to the office. It was, indeed, as aunty said, a blithe upcast to meet with; and I thought so, too, and often thought so, when dunting the pestle on the bottom of the brass mortar; for I hope ye have gotten a sufficiency of learning to understand that kirning drugs is braying in a mortar with a pestle, similar to the utensil which, as I have heard the one called, that stood above our door, gilded, the effigy of a doctor.

With Mr Junor, I was the best of three years; and it cannot be said, at the end of the term, that I was even then owre old to take my foot in my hand, to see what the world was like ayont the dyke. But it was a pleasant, sober time – the remembrance of it is lowne in my bosom, like a bonny April morning, when the buds biggen, and the birds begin to sing. Nor was my being in that odoriferous shop (as I heard the school-mistress one day call it) without profit, in a sense; for, at my work, I thought but of such a nice thing it must be to be rich, and used to lilt, in a cutty-crumb voice, keeping time with the pestle –

The king sits in his parlour,
Counting o'er his money;
The queen sits in her garden,
Eating bread and honey –

thinking his Majesty's duty was the pleasantest vocation of the two.

Nor, though Mr Junor might be an exact man, was he an Egyptian task-master, requiring bricks and giving no straw; for he was very considerate – which is more than can be said, as my experience teaches, of every one that has the repute of honesty in the world. Accordingly, he sometimes, of his own voluntary motion, gave me the play; and was sorry he could not do it on the Saturday afternoon, when the schools were skailed, as Saturday was, of a' the seven in the week, the throngest day in the Doctor's shop.

This James Junor, the druggist, though he lived among dry mint, thyme, and camomile, like a dead and stuffed alligator, was no an every-day body, but something by ordinar, and my heart warms yet when I think of him; for, though he lived by selling odious trash, his nature had no broo of any such commodities, he being a genteel man, and born, you would have thought, to be an ostentation in the world. But, now that I am well through life, I may say nothing is more common that to meet with a man whose nature is at war with his luck. The master was of this kind.

His father was a barber-man, in the High Street of Glasgow, near the College, and had the dressing of two Professors and the Principal, by which he acquired all the knowledge he had; but learning had little to do with it. In time, James got in, free gratis, to the classes, where he ettled so well that he was egged on to be a doctor; but when, however, he was in the middle of the strive, his father died of a sore income, and he was obligated to quit the College and to implement on chins. His heart, however, having a preeing of the light turns of doctoring, aye lay to that trade; and, in process of time, he got the druggist that then was in our town, to take him intil his shop, where, after mony a year as helper, he ripened, in the course of nature, to be his successor; and such he was, well stricken in years, when he took me on.

Besides being a druggist, James Junor was a good man; and one of the few I have ever seen that money was no required to make better. His wife, Mrs Junor, was not, however, either the yolk or kernel of womankind, but a mere woman – which is not saying a great deal in her behalf; but it's an auld observe, that the best of men have often the worst of wives, which, in my opinion, must be somehow a cause of their goodness; for, if they can thole the devil in the house, they'll no be overly fashed at any of God's creatures on the causeway. But, anent this head of discourse, however, I may as well keep a calm sough. Poor woman! she's long gone to her rest – and I'm sure she was not out of the need o't.

Letter IV

When I had been two years and a half with that gospel-hearted saint, Mr Junor, tholing as well's I could with his Jobish conjugality, and being nearing on the time to do for myself, I had some wiselike confabble with aunty.

It was agreed between us, that, as I had no prospect of being a robustious man, I should spouse my fortune as an errander in Glasgow. But the easiest trades are no without their craft – as may be seen by looking at watchmakers making faces at spectacle-eyes, as they keek by them into the bowelry of their commodities; so I could not set up as an errander in Glasgow, till I had learnt the outs and ins of that royal city. But, in this, Providence, as in all cases, was large; and the willing-to-do-well will never want a friend as long as there's a God in the Heavens.

It happened that aunty had a far-off cousin by her guidman's side – a well-doing weaver in the Gorbals; and he had a wife that was spoken of for that couthy kind of eidency which foretokens thriving; indeed, the truth of the saying has kythed on them, for, in the fulness of time, he was gathered to his fathers, in a bien way, and a bailie.

Well, it so happened that aunty got the schoolmaster to write a bit scrape of a pen to her kith, John Douce, and sent it by the Glasgow carrier, to tell him what I would be at, and how well I had behaved with James Junor. John was not long of making a response; for, when the carrier came back, he brought two lines from him, saying, he would do all in his potentiality to help me; and telling me no to be blate, but to come away and bide with him, making a recompense out of my earnings as I could afford it. Thus, it came to pass that, on my eleventh birthday, I went with the carrier to begin the world as an errander in Glasgow.

I cannot say I was very vogie on that morning of the venturing, when I bade farewell to aunty, and looked o'er my shoulder from the braehead at the town below. But I was so boun to be rich, that everything else was secondary; and the thought that I might be so in time, hampered the tear that was fain to creep into the corner of my eye. Still I could not but think of the times that were past; for, let our youth be never such a moil, there is something in the mysteries of the spirit that aye makes us look back upon't as on a blithesome morning.

Ye may think that to say so is rather more like a saft-horn than ye believe I am; but they look for trout in a shallow burn who dinna see that a man with an earnest intent has deep feeling. Do ye think I would ever had my dochter married to a lord, had I no got the upper hand of my human weakness, which was more than many would have liked to own? Na, na, my lad; ponder well, and warning take. I cared nae mair for wealth, for its own sake, than others; but I saw it was the key to all comforts, and to have my own will of them I in a sense coveted; but it was not the covetousness forbidden in the tenth commandment, for I never grudged no man his having. I only longed for the means by which I might conquest such havings. It was that power I sought to gain, by gaining riches – well knowing that with them I would get the potential; so dinna think I was either daft or doited, for I was no miser, but a man that saw gold ruled the world and only thought to make it a friend.

This observe is needful, now that I am telling you of what happened to me on the threshold of life; for, although ye maybe think, like many others, that I had never a right purpose, be ye assured that there is none without some aim – for, although we are not all alike in strength of will to do, we have the same likeness to each other in mind as we bear in body. And I dinna err in saying this; for, if ye dinna jalouse me to be of the niggardly order, you wouldna have been so bird-mouthed in the way you have asked for a 'replenishment'. Gair, Geordie, however, as you may think me, I never ettled for wealth but as a means; and, if you had the ee in your neck that I wish ye had, ye would see that. I had an early notion, that an onedicated man like me wasna the fittest to make a solid choice of the best butts and targets of fortune. I saw, however, that I couldna be far wrang if I got the means to win at any of them. So, if ye see, now and then, a bit glaik of fancy about me, no very like what ye thought, ye shouldna be surprised, or think in my auld days that I am putting on a new man, for I was aye the same; only, having long since conquered all my wants, I have grown slacker to make money in my age; indeed, my bairn, to tell you the truth, I have long made as much as I feel in myself capacity and fitness to use – and more would be fashious. As an earnest that I'm no at the grounds so foul as ye think, I send you enclosed a 'replenishment,' as you call it, on Tommie Coutts, to make good what I say, and to reprove your thoughts of me, if they need it.

Letter V

I weel mind the welcoming I got from John Douce and his wife. It couldna be said he was unjustly a narrow man; but he was, maybe, a thought hard. His wife, however, was a hand-waled woman, and had from the womb been ordained to bless the man she was made for.

We had some solid conversation anent what put it into my head to think of being an errand porter rather than a tradesman; and I replied that he might see I wasna of the right cut to be a prime tradesman, which was an admonishment no to try.

'Ay,' quo' the mistress, who had sat for some time before silent, 'guidman, he'll do weel, if that's his ain thought; for there's nothing helps on a man like a right knowledge of himself and what he's best fit for. The failures we meet with happen oftener from the man not knowing what he's fit for, than from want of ability. I aye doubt the thriving of those that itch for more than they seem to require.'

From less to more, we began to discourse together; and Mrs Douce spoke to me as if I was an experienced man, no only an auld-farrant wean, which was the most that could be said of me at home; and when I told her how I intended to make myself acquainted with the town before I set up in business, she said mony a pleasant thing about my having a discerning spirit.

The outcomings of that night I have never forgotten; for John Douce himself was a canny far-forecasting man; and, as for the mistress, I wonder how Nature was so thoughtless as to drop such a pearl, for the clutes and hooves of the multitude to tread on. Her heartening was a cordial that cheered me long, and made the dooly of my first night in the world as blithe as the banqueting of a baptism.

The next morning I rose betimes; and having covenanted with the carrier lad on the road, to shew me some of the town, we went hither and yon together till eight o'clock, in a very satisfactory manner. John Douce, after breakfast, having gone to the looms, his wife said that, as she was not very throng, she would go about with me, adding, it was aye to her a pleasaunce to help them that were so willing to do well. She was, indeed, a prudent woman, and very wisely thought that to make money was the true substantial way to do weel in this world.

I have often thought since that it was a wonderful thing how a woman of such sagacity had so much earnestness for a perfect wean; but she had none of her own, which partly may account for it: the promptings and spiritings of her own active nature was, however, no doubt, the main cause. Largely I profited by her pains; and, as we walked along the streets together, all her discourse was advices and admonitions. In short, my lines at the first with her fell in pleasant places, and she was a mother by common to me.

When I had learned myself well in the wynds and turns of Glasgow, I took my station aneath the pillars forenent the Tolbooth; but when I gaed home at breakfast time, a thought dowie because I had come no speed, Mrs Douce said it was not the right side of the street.

'One,' quoth she, 'should aye endeavour to begin the world on the right side of the causeway. It's no doubt a very creditable stance ye have taken; but it's no so good by a degree as the plainstones on the other side where the gentlemen congregate; – and, besides, ye must change that Kilmarnock bonnet. It gars you look of a country complexion. Do in Rome as they do in Rome; and mind never to make yourself kenspeckle unless it's in snodness; for maist folk, though they cannot tell why, have no broo of them that has onything out-o'-the-way about them.'

In consequence of this advice, I niffered after breakfast with another laddie for his hat with my bonnet and twopence, and took up my stance at a closs mouth wester the Tontine, which was then bigging;

the gentlemen, provost, and magistrates making then their houff at where the cross used to be, as I was told.

Good luck was in the change; for an Englisher soon after hired me to take a letter as far west as Madeira Court, and I made such nimble speed with the errand that he gave me a whole sixpence, the first white money I ever had received; in short, before the day was done, I had made a rough ninepence – that is, a bawbee over; and Mrs Douce, when I offered the half to John, would not let him touch it, saying that all I made the first day ought to be my own; for it was the luck arle of a fortune. It could not, therefore, but be said that I had a prospect in the very beginning.

Letter VI

The second day of my erranding, I mind weel, was not splendid; saving a twalpenny job to the Broomielaw, for a scrimping shopkeeper, to a Greenock gabbart, with the bundle of a Highland tartan plaid, belonging to a nauby that was going to Tobermory, I had but a scrimpit measure of luck. To be sure, towards the heel of the evening, a bailie, with a red north-west countenance, being vogie from his punchbowl and the funny stories of his cronies, hired me to go to Ruglen with a letter, on some 'lection ploy; for there was a great sough at that time of a Parlimenting, as it was called, which I have since learnt meant a general election. This achievement caused me to be in the gloaming before I got to John Douce's; and a weary wean I was, both with the length of the road and its sliddiness, caused by the forepart of the day being showery. Mrs Douce, seeing me so scomfished, took pains to hearten me, when I had rested myself, saying that there was no profit in running lang errands, and, therefore, I ought to eschew them.

'When ye're out o' the gait,' said she, 'far afield, like as to Ruglen, you may miss a shorter errand in the town, whereof the pay would be better, on a calculation; it would be hard, indeed, if the wage for twa hameart jobs were not as good as a runagate exploit to the country. Besides, there's a weariedness in a journey of one long continuance that's no to be coveted; one errand in the forenoon to sic like as Ruglen, does the best up for the remainder of the day.'

Thus she made it plain to my ordinary capacity, that the errand trade was, no more than the weavers' or the souters' trade, one of instinct, and that it behoved me to exercise my judgment in it as well as any other; for it had its craft as well as cabinet work. In a sense, the Ruglen 'lection job was thus no without its profit; for, after that day, they would have needed gleg een to see me on a toll road in the way of business.

But, although the erranding canna be said to be an ill ready-money business, when rightly followed out, it has its fasheries, as well as merchandizing; and I soon made an observe anent the same, which seems to shew what a wonderful regularity there is in all the works of Providence; and that was, that, counting by the days, it had a degree of uncertainty, proving it ought not to be trusted; but, taking the earnings by the week together, it was more of a dependance; and, by the month, it was as good as a stated income, which you of the genteeler orders have no notion of. In short, before I was anything like half a year on the pavý of the Trongate, as I once heard a playactor man call the planestanes, the jingle of my peinor pig told, in sterling language, that erranding was an effectual calling, though, maybe, no just a coining of money; nor did I repent I had taken it up. As the winter, however, came on, with short days and long nights, I had my experience, that, like everything of a human nature, it had its blemish of onagreeables – particularly in the dark days of November, on which I discerned, that, although the morning and the forepart of the day could not be objected to, the hinder end and the evening was always obstrapulous and showery, when porters, and erranders who are kind of 'prentices to them, are fain to howff and harbour in close mouths and other places, that, at times, would not be the waur of a souping, cuddling themselves with their hands in their bosoms or in their pouches.

Nevertheless, for all the wind and the sleet that we were exposed to, the first winter was won through, with an ettle; and when the fine, sunshiny spring mornings came round, there was mirth in my veins; and the skies, taking off their cloudy fause-faces, looked well pleased on the earth, new-washen with the growing showers.

In short, I cannot complain very sincerely of the time I spent in Glasgow; but, when I had got the upper hand of my fifteen year, I left it; and, ye may be sure, I would never have done so, had I no been wiled away by a glaik of hope that promised to make me better; no, maybe, of a bible betterness – I'll no say that – but in the circumstances; and the cause of the come to pass, I will presently rehearse.

In the meantime, speaking of my departal from Glasgow, it is but a duty incumbent to say that I staid the whole time I was there, with

John Douce and his wife; for baith were kind, discreet folk. The mistress, however, was the honey bee; for, although John was an eident, gair creature, he had never the gumption of his rib; and he would have been content to moil on in mediocrity, had she not been blest with a discernment past common. Afterwards, when the thrive of the late war began to sprout, and I heard how they were topping, well I knew wha put the spunk to the peat, and snodded the hearthstone. It was the mistress. Oh! she was a managing woman, and a sorrow for egging on her guidman, who would have been content to have gotten through life with an insignificance, but for her, who was really upsetting, and saw the right ways o't. In short, I had a peinor pig full of dollars, and, had there been a Saving Bank in yon times, I'll no say but what I might have found the way to it; for, besides a silver watch, to tell me what o'clock it was, I had mair than seven pounds to the fore for a sair foot, when the time ordained was out at Glasgow.

Letter VII

Never being of a strong make, I was not made for hard work; and having, by the time I was in my fourteen, seen that, one year with another, I could not expect to make gold in gowpens at the erranding in Glasgow, I began to cast about for a new line. A sturdy porter I could not be, by reason of my weak back, for that with a careful man is no an ill way; but an errander, which, though for a callant it has a feasibility of a competency, is, upon the whole, for a grown-up man, but a cold coal to blaw at; so, seeing that I must soon deval from the erranding, and couldna be a porter to carry heavy trunks and boxes, I made up my mind for a change; and thus I soon had an experience of what I have often since noticed in life – namely, that it's never long till the chance casts up of getting the thing the mind's set on.

As I entered my fifteen, there was a family with their chattels and chairs going by the Liverpool traders from Greenock to Manchester, where trade was brightening; and they, jalousing that the Englishers could not be so good as our own sober folk, wanted a man of the lad speshy to go round with their things, offering good pay for the turn. Thus it came to pass that I got a preferment. I had indeed the repute for being an obligatory creature, with a willing heart and a pawkie blithe tongue.

The going to Manchester did not appear to be such a very desperate going out of the Christian world as John Douce thought when I first spoke of it to him. His guidwife had very rational notions on the subject, saying that 'surely Manchester couldna be so kittle to a hobbledehoy of fifteen, as Glasgow had been to a foreign laddie of ten, with bare feet and an innocency.' And thus it came to pass that I covenanted with Mr Nichol Spreul to go with him and his plenishing to Manchester, he paying me days' wages.

When the gear was on board the gabbart, and the master and the mistress away with the fly, me, and the servan lass, and the four weans went down to the Broomielaw and took shipping in the same gabbart, from which we were landed safe at the mid-quay of Greenock, nigh to the Liverpool packet ordained for the family; when, without any great ettering of fash, we got all our rickle of things put on board, a full day before the Perseverance, as the trader was called, could be ready; by which I had time to look about me and to make observes on Greenock and the inhabitants thereof; or rather feuars and subfeuars, as I saw them spoken of in a proclamation on the corner of a house, which one Sir Michael Stewart, Bart., had put out, to admonish them anent something concerning a steeple then about to be biggit on a kirk that the bailies had put up for one Sir John Shaw.

Greenock, it cannot be honestly said, was in yon days, whatever may be said of it now, just a marrow for Glasgow, though it had a Bell entry that was not ill-faured; but, if the streets to the westward were not paved like those of the New Jerusalem, with precious stones, it must be allowed that there was no want of herring heads to be seen on them; and as for rain, there was a sufficiency for a calamity to every other person but to folk accustomed to make their living by the sea, which the Greenock folk surely are. I observed that it was not true that the childer, as was said of them in Glasgow, were all and every one web-footed. Na, the Glasgow bairns are more web-footed, their fathers in general being weavers.

It was not concerning the oddities of the place, however, that, in my day of idleness, I was chiefly taken up with; for I got a new light from what I saw there that was as precious ointment to me among the Englishers.

It seemed that a seaport was a real fine place to set up as a porter in, so many strangers coming by the shipping behoving to have help because of their strangeness. And this notion barmed and worked in my noddle all the voyage to Liverpool, and was of a great outcoming; for the first thing I did, when we got afterwards to Liverpool, was to look with a scrutinizing eye about me, regarding this very thing, insomuch that, before Mr Spreul got his commodities off to Manchester, I had made up my mind to make a trial of Liverpool, as a place of bread; for I had seen that an inward town would not be so expedient to set up in, for the line I intended, as an emporium. In landward towns, like Manchester – which was like Glasgow, as I was told – every creditable concern had its feed porter; but the like of Greenock and Liverpool had more of a dishevelment.

This was a thought of wisdom, for out of it grew all the kything of my fortune that I want you to learn the particulars of, and for which I am inditing these epistles; for the moral I would make, is, that a man should well consider things before he makes his downseat. Not, however, to tire you with outs and ins, ye see that my capacity was growing as I grew aulder, and that I was not without an understanding before I even got so far into the world as Liverpool.

Letter VIII

When I had gotten Mr Spreul and his perafarnals, as I maun call his family and fasheries, weel housed at Manchester, I came back on shanks' naggy to Liverpool – for I had no thought then to cess myself with a boutger of a horse, like you, no having a grandfather that I could write to for a 'replenishment;' and I set up business there as I had weel before devised.

I had not, however, been long in a way till I was led to make an observe, that the Englishers, compared with right Scotch folk, are a desperate set for being het and fu'. It is weel for the poor amang them that they have the parish pock-neuk to gang to.

What led me to make this notandum, was a fatty sort of man that was a porter on the quays and wharfs. He had a swelled muckle toe, by reason of the gout; with which there never was a man that bore a burthen fashed, it's my belief, in all the ancient realm of braid Scotland. Indeed, it's no a malady that messes or mells with hard-working folk, but is a gentle distemper, rife only among them whose wives paint their faces as if they could thereby scog their sinfulness; for it is well known they have much need to hide their shame, if all tales be true.

This man with the sore toe was an object to me which I narrowly and 'cutely scrutinized; for he seemed to have the gleggest and weel-doingest laddie weans for a family of the male gender I ever saw –

wonderfully, as I thought, all of an eildens. He himself did nothing but sit on a stone from morning to night, and take orders for errands, on which he sent his gets, as I thought them; by which I could see he made a power of money, really siller like sclate-stanes. By and by, however, I began to come to the rights of it, and learnt in time that the callants were not of his own clecking, but taken on as servitors, 'cause of his being a lamiter; and that he paid them a wage, making a bein living of the owercome.

When I reached the depth of this mystery, and had thought with myself of taking up the same way of business, there came an Irish gentleman from Limerick – a wee he was of the flaunty order; and was going to London town to set up a trade of selling pork in barrels, beef in tierces, and firikens of butter, to say nothing of neats' tongues. Seeing me of a composed stature and a creditable complexion, he offered to take me as his porter, and I agreed to go; for I had ever a forethought that London was ordained for me. To be sure, it would have been far from a sober Scotsman's hand to have hired an Irishman on the quays of Liverpool for ony sic job; but the Irish have their own ways – that are, perhaps, no ill for those that ken how to make them serve their turn. Thus it came to pass, that, before I had long sojourned in Liverpool, I was taken to London to see to Mr O'Gommarel's kegs o' provisions; and there began my fortune to lay golden eggs, like the goose that I mind reading of at the school in a history book.

Mr O'Gommarel, being a gentleman, went in a coach, and I, being only a porter, coggled on the top of it; but we fell in with no accidence – only an Irish wife was there that would fain have made up to me, so that I jalouse she was of the clans of the city of Dublin.

However, in course of nature, to London we did at last get, and homolgomates ourselves in Ratcliff Highway, opening a warehouse for Irish provisions, with every prospect of doing great things. But long we were not there when Mr O'Gommarel took a calamity intil his head which proved a brain fever; and, from less to more, he became a useless man, and for a time I knew not what to do. At last, he was taken away, clean daft, home to his friens in the city of Limerick, and I was left like a knotless thread ganging hither and yon in London for a time.

What might have come of me in that strait of fortune, is not to be told; but it happened that, in consequence of Mr O'Gommarel's by-set, there was a gentleman that took charge of the store; and he, seeing me a wiselike lad, elected me to take charge of it and sell off, as soon as I could, the cargoes that Mr O'Gommarel told me himself would help to make his fortune.

This trust I performed with a sincerity, accounting for every doit to the gentleman that the provisions brought, learning myself the first cost of the commodities, and what could be made by them in the way of profit and loss in Ratcliff Highway.

Thus, without any divination on my part, I was led cannily into the provision line. But I have something to tell of my traffickings before I ripened into full bloom; for the summer was warm, corbies might have been seen shooting out their tongues, and the fairings for sale on my staun being salt, the traffic in them ebbed down to a naething in the warm months.

Letter IX

Hinging on in a sort of idleset all day in the store with Mr O'Gommarel's provisions, I had more time than was just profitable for to make a meditation anent the nearest way to take in going to Lucky Fortune's tabernacle. While I was in this posture, the labouring men of the neighbourhood sometimes daunered in for a crack now and then; by the which they got an inkling of the nature of my business, learning that I bout to have now and then a pound or two no wanted; as I had but to sell, and to buy nothing, for I did not, in the slack of the season, settle every week with Mr Boyle, the gentleman that had the doing, as was my wont when trade was lively. Thus it came to pass that a new light broke in upon me that was truly a godsend. The way of it was this: –

There was a weel-doing man, who used to get his wage by the half-quarter, who had eight dochters, every one of whom had a brother, as he told me. He was, however, a thought pawkie; for the dochters, and their having each a brother, made but nine children; whereas I, of a naturality, fancied that there was sixteen of them – eight laddies and eight lassies; and had, by consequence, a sore compassion for his small family, and used to think often with dolorosity concerning them even in the kirk.

One day he came to me, and said as how his employer was gone to Hull, and would not be back for a week; by which he was put to a pinch, as his wage was due and he knew not what to do – begging of me the loan of a pound note, saying he would pay it back, with a shilling for the accommodation, next week, when his employer came home.

Being wae for the poor man, with his heavy handful of eating moths constantly devouring, I gave him the pound note on tick; telling him he need not be particular about the usury, but only to be sure and pay me the pound. Weel, when the master came home, he paid the note like an honest man, and the shilling likewise, as a gentleman should; whereat I was not ill pleased. This was the mustard-seed that grew in time to be the great tree; for, when I was at my meditations in the cellar, thinking of this and that, the thought of the pound and the usury came uppermost; and I considered with myself that, if I could so lend, I would soon make my plack a bawbee; so, by littles and littles, I creepit into the banking line, as usury is called by the genteeler orders. My dealings, however, were at first with those in an ordinar' station of life – working tradesmen, and such like. Thus it came to pass that, before Mr O'Gommarel's provisions were all sold, I had made, as ye may say, a penny more than my wage, having weel on to thirty pounds over and aboon hainings.

In the time I was thrang with idleset at the salt provisions, in warm weather, I made another prime reflection, which was of vast use to my prosperity; and I beg, Geordie, you'll take tent of the same – and that was, I lookit weel about me at the conduct of those said to be doing weel in the world; by which I discerned that there was a something no man could weel thrive without.

They were all sober, prudent, and honest folk. Hempies, I saw, might cut a galore for a season, but they sooner or later proved peoies and pluffs in the pan; whereas your real, sterling, cut-and-come-again characters were discreet men, who kent full well how many blue beans it takes to make five, and made a conformity thereunto.

I saw, likewise, that they were all harnisht in the conjugal yoke; though some of them, maybe, didna count marriage a matter of money; but those that did best were methodical lads, married upon elderly widows with a nest egg, whereon they clockit to some purpose: so it was from them that I resolved to take a pattern. I'll no deny, however, that there were decent weel-doers among them that werena just so particular, taking up with lassies for a fancy; but all, both the widow-mongers and the tender-hearted, were most extraordinar' fond of their own firesides; which led me to conclude that, if a man ettles to do right in the world, he maun learn to think that hame's aye hamely; as I shall shew forth by the example of James Hobart, who was a non-plus among the acquaintances of my threshold days, for so I accounted the green strivings of my youth.

Letter X

James Hobart was a lad from the country; and, by reason of no other trade being in his village, was naturally a wheelwright. In his 'prenticeship, he foregatherit with one Harriet Lees, a weel-faured lassie that did turns about his master's house, by which it came to pass that he took a notion of her long before he was out of his time; and so it happened that, in the summer gloamings, him and her used to walk Damon-and-Phillising about the dyke-sides. In this jeopardy, it so fell out that an auld aunty that bonny Harriet had on Tower Hill, fell ill of an income in her legs, by which she was obligated to have somebody with her; and, no approving of the loup-the-dyke cattle of London, she, this frail woman, sent for Harriet – and Harriet came to her.

James Hobart was, about this season, on the finishing of his 'prenticeship, and knowing that he would soon have the upper hand of his 'denture, he made a preparation to follow; little thinking but London was a town for wheelwrights as good as Clearbrook. But he was mistaken, for there are no wheelwrights in London; and, for that matter, though I have been so long in it, I never saw a wheel or a reel for lint or tow therein. So, when James came and had seen his jo, ne'er a turn of work could he get to do; and he wandered about like a demented creature, ae bawbee going out of his pocket after another, as if they were trying how soon he could be brought to beggary.

One day, while he was very waeful, with nothing but the barren street before him, he happened to pass a blockmaker's shop-door; at the sight of which he had an inspiration. It seemed to him that there was a fitness between blockmaking and wheelwrighting that might by a little pains be brought into fellowship; so he went in, and confabbled with the man before he came out; and the upshot was, that James was taken in, and from that day and hour the world never gaed back with him. So, in process of patience, the fractious aunty departed, as she hoped herself, into Abraham's bosom, and James espoused his darling dagon, Harriet.

They had, as need not be told, only a cauld coal to blaw at; but they had a fine bleezing ingle of mutual affection: so they set to and warsled with the world, which they at last got the better of, and had sons and daughters. They were not, however, just marigolds, shining far and aye kenspeckle, but douce folk; and I had great satisfaction in sometimes, on a Sabbath night, drinking a dish of tea with them, for we sat in the same pew at the meeting.

Thus was I led to make an observe, that all who do well go regularly to the kirk; and James and his winsome marrow never missed a day. So they came into prosperity; and when he died, last year, soon after his wife, he was far ben in the world, having been all his days a credit both to his kith and kin, and his three buirdly sons masters of vessels.

Taking by times James Hobart for a patron, I soon saw that, if I expected to prosper, there was no help for it, but to marry a wife; and I began to cast about for a good one; but for a season I came little speed at the fishing. Howsever, I had learnt, by Mr O'Gommarel's provisioning, that, with a thought of canniness, I could turn a better penny on my own pook-neuk in the banking line than by being subject to the hither and thither of any master; so, when the store was toomed, I grew more intent to get an equal than a superior; which was the cause of my becoming a guidman; by which, as you shall hear by and by, you are the son of my dochter, and in the land of the living, seeking a replenishment, and keeping devouring horses at the College, where it would be more to your advantage, maybe, if you read the Scriptures.

However, Geordie, as ye cannot but be interested to hear how it came to pass that I got lawfully a dochter, the whom in time came to have a kittling, whilk was you, I will let this letter go by the post mail, and in another rehearse more particularities.

Letter XI

Being in a way of trial, and seeing that the way to thrive was to be happily married, and to go to the kirk regular, making my home at my own fireside, I had a meditation thereanent; and I saw that, although there might be a cosiness in the lot of siclike as James Hobart, there was likewise a peradventure; so, not being overly likely to be taking to a maiden's ee, I resolved on making a prudent choice. It's wonderful how Providence helps a man, when he has wrought himself into a resolution, especially if the drift o't be weel-doing.

I had not been long matured in the thought that I ought to marry, when there was an upcast from Providence, shewing a good-will towards mine intent. Going now and then on the Sunday to take a dish of tea with James Hobart and his helpmeat – for she was truly that – it fell out one night that a decent woman of the widow gender, not too well stricken in years for me, also was there at her tea. Her guidman had been a sail-maker in Liverpool, and she was sib herself to Mrs Hobart, which was the cause of her apparition there; for he being dead and gone, she had come to resident in Radcliff Highway, and was very lonely, being new in widowhood; for which cause she was invited to make a pass-over of her weariness, by coming to take her tea.

As soon as I saw Mrs Canvas, though I was more than seventeen years younger, I had an instinct, and said to myself, Please God, this shall be my commodity. And really we passed a very conversible afternoon. Towards the gloamin, however, the skies began to gloom; but as it turned out, that was the way Providence blithened on what it had ordained to come to pass; for, about the time for Mrs Canvas to go home, there was an evendown pour, and it rained and better rained, as if the windows of heaven were opened, and the angels had been washing their dwelling; so that it behoved me to go home with her, to scog her from detriment with an imbreley, which was covenanted. But, as we crouched along, the waters were none assuaged, and there came on such a pour of wet, that if, in mercy, an entry had not been opened to us, into which we sheltered, it's no saying to what shifts we would have been driven. However, into the closs-mouth we went, and long we stood together there; but not a dawn of hope kythed. Wet, wet it was, and Mrs Canvas thought of home, giving me to understand that, if I had been her guidman, she would not have objected to go with me to rest ourselves intil a public.

Hearing this, I said, in a consolatory manner, that truly a woman who had been married, was, by reason of widowhood, in a lanerly condition; and, from less to more, we thickened into an understanding; insomuch that, when it faired, I saw her safe home, and called the next morn's morning to speer if she was none the worse of the blattering. In short, having heard from James Hobart, that Mrs Canvas had a something, I made her my polar star; and, no to waste words, we were by and by married. But, for all that, she was not your grandmother; for she had not been my guidwife scarcely a twelvemonth and a day, when she took a kittling in her craig, and departed this life at her appointed time with a sore heart – a kink as it were – leaving me all her residue, which was a good penny, more than double and aboon for what I married her; but she said I had made the best of husbands, and needed a consolation for the loss of her: so saying, she died, leaving me with the meal, though the basin was taken away.

Letter XII

Seeing myself, by the blessing of God, and the removal of my wife, in a state of mair business than I ever thought to be in, I again began to think how I could best cast my bread upon the waters; so, having learned something of how to do in the provisioning, I set myself – for, as it were, a pastime in my doleful widowhood – once more among the casks and kegs of a store of beef and pork; and for more than twelve months, if I didna make gold in gowpens, I turned the penny; which, with my banking, made it no an ill trafficking I had taken up.

It was then I had a preeing of the world; for, as my means grew, and my profits kittled both by the store and the lending of money for a consideration, I had an insight of men's bosoms. Many's the Nebuchadnezzar of the Royal Exchange that has had his ain straits, that, in my day, I have helped. They used to gang by me on Cornhill with a dry civility in their looks, and a pawkie fearfulness in their secret eyes, that told me, though they hid it from the world, how much they were beholden to my wife's residue. The seeing of this made me gleg; and at last I could tell, by the way of a squint, whether a man was going up or stoitering down the hill. It's really wonderful to think of the key ye get to men's bosoms when you lend them money. Mind this, and think weel of the consequence, my man, Geordie, when your pouch is yawp for a 'replenishment.'

However, it wasna in learning just the ways of the world that I was industrious, for I was a thought maybe commendable in all things, especially as, before the second year of by doleful widowhood, I began to see that my purse could bide to be shaken in the teeth of an ordinar gale of wind, and that even my superiors once, were, if not inferior, maybe no better than equals.

In this tining and winning there came a to-pass of which it's right I should set down and make mention; for, in the beginning, it did not kythe to my advantage: but it is ordained that good shall come out of evil.

Being, you see, thriving in the provision line, I thought I would enlarge; for, by this time, I had made an observe that, whomsoever in

London dealt in eatables and drinkables, and is well-doing in the ways of private conduct, is sure to fen; so I gave an order to my correspondents in Limerick, Cork, and Belfast, to send me an augmentation of their articles in the fall of the year. The reason of my having correspondents for the same things in different places, was this, that they might not be led to think of making their conjectures about the stroke of business I did. Thus it fell out, that, about Martinmas time, which is the season for slaying bullocks and stots, my neighbours, seeing I was getting cargoes, and having a high opinion of my canniness, resolved to get cargoes too, by which the market was glutted, as the saying is, like a churchwarden eating the bastard child of a married man that can afford to pay for it; and thus it came to pass, that some of these speculators, no having their pockets so well lined as mine, were put to sad shifts for the needful, as their bills payable came due. I jaloused that this would be the case, but waited on, keeping a calm sough. No, howsever, to simmer and winter about it, I got many a sappy bargain from them, both of salt beef and pork, in the spring of the year, to say nothing of what I had laid in myself – the cause of all. Indeed, I began to have compunctions of spirit that I was beguiled to my undoing, by reason of so many bargains; but the Lord aye prospers the well-doing with prosperity, and just in the nick of time there came out a rumour of war anent the Falkland Islands, by which the price of Irish provision, was increased, and I got off all I had briskly, without a detriment, maybe with a bawbee of profit. Well it was that I had shewn such a sagacity; for, in a short time, the news of the war diminished away, and those who bought my goods were pushed what to do with them, although they were accounted sicker souls.

By this affair I got a repute that was as good as much profit. It was seen by the handling I made of the job, that I could see as far into a nether millstone as most people; and thus it came to pass, that I grew to be in much esteem with my neighbours, some of whom thought they were of the seed of Isaiah the prophet, and prognosticated that there were signs about me of one ordained to gather the residue of the fruits of the earth as they kythe in the bit rags of bank notes.

Letter XIII

By the time my Falkland Island job, as I call that rehearsal just mentioned, was turned into sterling, there was an elderly decent man, of few kindred, with an only dochter, that I fell into some acquaintance with. She, as you shall be told, came to be your grandmother.

This Mr Marling was a discreet man; and having few down-draughts, his bit gathering was not the worst thing in London town. It therefore attracted us into a cordiality; and I saw that his sonsy only dochter had many points of haivins that showed gumption. In short, in a reasonable time, we were married; and she, being of a genteel turn, I did not make an objek to her taking a genteel house, because, with her prospect, and what I had in the foot of the stocking, we could afford it. So, thus, I came to be transported into a sphere of life that was not thought of in the days of erranding at Glasgow.

But, saving the exploit of the marriage, and the getting of a child, which was your mother, and which we were not very long about, I cannot say that there was much variorum in my way of life for several years. I saw that, with canny handling, there was outcoming in the provision line: so I keepit on for an ostentation. But the best spoke in my wheel, and it made little cheeping, was the discounting, after all; the beginning of which, as I have rehearsed, had only the chance of a shilling.

By my clecking with what I had, and old Mr Marling's frugality at gathering, before your mother, my only dochter, came to be six, there there were not wanting fools who said that I was a warm man; and, surely, it would be an onthankful acknowledgemnt to deny I had not prospered in all things by my judicious circumspection. At this juncture, however, it was ordained in the councils of eternity, that a golden tree should surely shoot for my behoof; and, accordingly, it so fell out. Mr Marling, my guidfather that was, on day coupit o'er off his seat in a 'poplexy, and left to your mother, that was his oe, twenty thousand pounds, and a residue to me and my wife that was worth the lifting off the midden with a pair of tongs. The fact is, that nobody had a notion he would cut up to the tune he did; for it was on the right side of fifty thousand.

There had been a graduality of respect towards me for some time – I was sensible of that; but really the outcoming of reverence that followed on the death of Mr Marling, was just extraordinary; telling me that, let your men of poeticals say what they will, there's no endowment of nature equal to the dripping roast of a fat legacy. But, Geordie, mind now what I say.

Riches I never thought of but as the means to get the mastery of the good things of life; and, therefore, I saw when Mr Marling's hoggart fell among us, it was no longer required of me to be so methodical in my 'conomy as I had been; so I gave consent to my wife to take a fine house; and, as she then began to complain of the rheumatism in her legs, it would not have been Christian to have stood out overly dourly against having a carriage of our own, 'specially when the doctor gave it as his advice that it would do her no harm.

But, although, from our flitting intil that house, it couldna be said that the warld gaed back with me, there was an increase of fasheries that I did not expect. But, in those days, mony a braw man kent what it is to be powdered; and so it was with me. I could complain of no ail; but they little ken what the calamities of life are, that have never felt a youky head because of mity powder.

Letter XIV

Your grandmother was a by-ordinar woman for natural sagacity – in that way, she might have been the marrow of Mrs Douce of Glasgow; so, as soon as we were well settled in our new house, she said to me, one night, as we were in our bed, talking composedly of this and that – the weather being very warm, by reason whereof we could not sleep – that she thought there was a prudence in making use of the means God gave, as well as in gathering them; and that, since we could afford to act as well as our neighbours, we would be looked down on if we did not.

I said that that was my very opinion; and, therefore, while I looked after the traffic, I would trust to her eidency to see to the house. Thus a sort of a silent 'pact and covenant grew up between us; and she went, and came, and said, and did, in all manner of matters of householding, as seemed good in her own eyes; by which, she being a woman of commonsense – which I understood, from some of my friends, is a very rare things in wives – we had a lowne time o't.

Thus it happened that an exploit came uppermost, that well deserves a place in the chronicles; for there was an instance in it of great prudence, the which my wife often thought was just extraordinar, considering my natural parts, as they had been brought out by an yedication no particular. It concerned our only dochter, Mary, your lady mother, at that time little better than a playoc bairn.

You see, when, after my guidfather had won away, with a direck circumbendibus, into Abraham's bosom, I made a count and reckoning with the wife, of all that we then had in the hoggart; and the upshot was, that we thought we might take, as I have set forth, a new house; and, as a carriage is surely a great saving to shune and clothes in wet weather, to say nothing of the solacium of it at all times, we resolved that we might do a waur turn in our time than set up one for an economy – which, at the flitting, we did: it gied, however, to my heart to use it, save when the lift was high, the sky blue, and the sun clear.

When we had gotten the chaise, I had a meditation with myself; and I saw that my wife, owing to the straitened way she had been brought up, and likewise that, as my own schooling was not college lair, our get might ettle at a better refinement; so I said that, as the Lord had blessed our basket and our store with a moderation, we ought to take the sanctified use of things. The guidwife cordially agreed with me that it would be a becoming testimony of thankfulness so to do; and I accordingly hinted to her, that, being sensible of our own deficiencies, we should put Clemy into a boarding school, to learn manners and to play on the spinnet. To this there was a most pleasant assent; but the guidwife would not allow that she herself had been educated in a straitened circumstance – though she could not but see that I had not been brought up at the feet of Gamaliel. Anent this, however, there was no controversy; for I had often observed that leddies schooled to narrow breeding, are aye the most logive, and make up for being scrimply thought of by the rest of the world, by thinking muckle of themselves; so, for peace in the house, and glad to get Clemy in a way to take on a pedigree education, I minded the auld guess, that what the rich put in their pouches, the beggars throw awa; and I made the affront a pocket napkin.

Boarding schools for bits of lassies that have a prospect are no that ill to find; therefore, we soon got a very prime one; but I would not hear of it; for there was in it a lord's daughter, and I was a thought blate to let a bairn of mine rampauge with a cutty of nobility. So we gave it the go-by – and well it was that we did; for we got an inkling of a capital leddy in the country, an offisher's widow by lot, and a dean's dochter by nature, forbye being a woman of a share of mother's wit, and a most accomplished character.

To her house, after some negociation, I took your mother, in our own vekle, and were well pleased with Mrs Mortimer, who was surely a most particular leddy, and had all in her domicile on chandler pins. My wife gave her many directions concerning how she thought Clemy should be brought up. In this, however, I thought she was rather inordinate, and said, maybe a wee shortly –

'Mrs Mortiner, ye see we're hamely folk, and it has pleased Providence to give us something for our dochter; so make her, as well as ye can, fit to use it discreetly, and we'll never say ye were slack.'

The leddy was confounded; and she looked at me with an inquisitive eye, and replied –

'Sir,' said she, 'I do not wonder that a man who thinks so well has prospered in the world.'

When my wife heard a lady of such breeding say so, I could see a change, and, maybe, more respect for my opinion, on her part, than was very kenspeckle before; for, like other married women, she certainly had not, till this time, always a gospel reverence for her breadwinner's condescendence and discernment.

Letter XV

In the meantime, there was no backwardness in the world with me; for I, being accounted to have elbow-room, had a nerve for an advantage. On one settling day on the Stock Exchange, I made a rough penny on all the best part of my gathering, as well as on Clementina's legacy, for which maybe a puirer man would be more thankful. It was thus.

For some time before, there had been a sough from the parish of France, anent convention doings there, by which men of a discerning spirit saw a hobbleshow barming – and so I thought too; and in consequence gave out that I had a something to lend on mortgage, not thinking the funds the best of investments.

This notification caused many a right honourable and other of landed pedigree, to make application; and, in short, I saw a way of laying out every plack and bawbee I had scraped together, over and aboon my dochter's gratis gift, by way of wadset for a time, to good advantage. Seeing this, without thinking of the French convention, I made up my mind to sell out. No other thought had I but to raise the needful for my own ends. But it was soon known, to the consternation of bulls and bears, that I was turning all my stock, even my dochter's, into money; then everybody thought I had got an inkling of something no canny, and the hobbleshow that was the consequence was dreadful, after it was known that I had really sold all. Some said the King of France, that afterwards got his head chappit off, had been obligated to drink aquafortis. In short, the Stock Exchange was in a commotion, like as it sometimes is; down fell the stocks, down, down, and up flew many a broker's eye, till ye could discern only the white thereof, all owing to me and the wadset intention.

As the fall took place after I had sold out, I had a great plant at my banker's. I began to think – especially as, at the close of the market, it began to spunk out that the latest news from France were rather of a 'healthy tint' – that the panic might be from my operations. I said, however, nothing, keeping my own counsel even from the guidwife, for there are things that wives at times should not be conjunct in.

Next morning, I was down at the opening. All looked well; but there was now and then a little waver, shewing, it maybe, a shade of difference upwards.

Then was my time – I bought a few thousand. No sooner had I done so, than the tidings flew that I had made a spec. In came buyers on buyers, droves on droves, as well informed as a flock of sheep louping a dyke; up jumped the stocks, like merryandrews on the slackwire, and before twelve o'clock the reaction was full one and five-eights above what I had sold at; so I bought in for money, and sold for the account, whereby I got creeshy paws to lick without any outlay of mind. But it was not so thought; and I was, of course, reckoned to be one of the slyest fox-paws in the city; it being the whole sprose of the day, how cleverly I had managed; of which there can be no doubt, as those that said so were considered guid judges. In short, I became into such repute, that divers brokers came from Lombard Street, bowing and cringing, asking me to join their old established firms.

Letter XVI

From the time I had entered into the banking line, when my chance was only a shilling, I thought it necessar to look weel into the characters and capacities of men; and I soon discerned that it was a custom of bankers to hold their heads higher than merchants, and to snuff the east wind with round and wide nostrils. But I likewise saw, although they were as the golden images in papistical kirks, muckle-made-o' things, yet that the merchants, after all, were like the priests, using them for their own advantage, and, in short, were the bees that made the honey.

I cannot say, however, that their gesticulation, in the way they shot out their snouts, gave me an inordinate conceit of their judgments as human creatures; indeed it's the nature of banking operations to spawn small ideas; for the tradesmen themselves have only to think if their customers be of an ability to endure a certain time.

This consideration of durability breeds a constipation of the understanding; and no doubt it is because they are so afflicted with it that nobody who can help it likes to see the front of them at a board where any measure of understanding is required.

As for the merchants, poor dependant things – for even when they get their bills done, the inward gladness of their hearts is aye mollified with a humiliation – they are much to be pitied. I never see one of them guffawing, and eagerly kilfudyocking with a banker, saying the craw's white, as he says it, without being duberous of his credit. Catch me, Geordie, melting the bills of such nichering cattle, though I may be wae for their extremities. But, to make an end, however, I never greened to be otherwise than on a guid-e'en and guid-day footing with my banker, for fear of my credit; as I jaloused others in the world might see with the tails of their een as well as me. Nevertheless, my exploit on the Stock Exchange made some noise; and it's wonderful to think how wise I grew: as everybody said, I was just in a sense a wee Solomon.

And thus it came to pass that I ne'er was a partner in a ostentatious banking house: at which many marvelled; but I minded what I had heard aunty say when I was only saft in the horn: – 'There's no telling,' quo' she, 'when twa heads are on the bolster, by whilk the guid or the ill luck comes.' In like manner, thought I, there's no telling who is the cause of making the siller in a partnership. Therefore, all my days I eschewed to go marrows with anybody, 'cepts the guidwife; and with her, ye ken, I could not help it, being ordained from the foundations of the world to the conjugal yoke.

But, although I had no broo of your company concerns, there was an outcoming in my prosperity that weel deserves to be noticed, especially for the heartening it gave the guidwife, who, like all helpmeats of thriving characters, liked to have a share of the gains. And it fell out in this way. Just on the back of my Stock Exchange exploit, the alderman of our ward took the gout in his belly, the day after the 9th of November, and was, on the 10th, in Abraham's bosom; by which there came to be a vacancy in the court of aldermen.

As soon as it was known that he was departed, several gentlemen came to my door and finding me not at home, they said they would pay their respects to Mrs Plack, who had a good repute for sagacity in the neighbourhood; and being let in to her by the flunkie, they told her, with a dolorous voice, what a calamity had befallen the ward, inquiring if she thought I would allow myself to be sheriff, as it was minded to make one of the sheriffs his successor. She thereupon answered and said, that, as it was an honour, to be sure I ought to accept, and that her endeavours to persuage me would not be to seek. So, when I came home, I heard of the deputation, ye may be sure: but it's necessar to tell you all about it, for Mrs Plack's heart was set on it, and therefore she thought it was a case needful of a particular cooking.

Letter XVII

Coming home to my dinner that day, as I was telling, after the deputation had been seeing how the land lay, I could discern that there was a gale in the cat's tail. Mrs Plack was going up and down, speaking loud and often to the servants, and had seemingly a great turn in hand, though I could not see't. She never, however, opened her lips to me, but had dinner served in less than no time and a jiffy; and I could see, for I have a discernment when onything's gaun on by common, was most instantaneous to have the lad out of the room, and ourselves, in the secrecy of cabinet ministers, as was seen when the table was drawn.

'Mr Plack,' said she – which was the more remarkable as her use and wont was to call me only Plack – 'Mr Plack, I have been thinking that life is but in our life, and that we are all life-like and yet doomed to die. There's Mr Alderman Gravy – he is released from the troubles of this world, and his place must be filled up. What is your opinion of the accident?'

I, being as innocent as a lamb of the cabal, but having heard when I was out of the Alderman's calamity, replied that it was indeed a hasty warning to be moderate.

'Moderate!' cried she – 'I was saying nothing of that; but only observing it was a thing to be considered.'

'No doubt, my dear,' quo' I, 'it cannot but cause a reflection.'

'Snuffies!' said she, tartly. 'It would not ill become a man of your substance to think of some one fit to be his successor. Londin, depend on't, cannot do without an Alderman; and Sheriff Stew, it is said, will be his successor; so that there will be a vacancy in the sheriffdom.'

Still in perplexity, I said, no knowing what I said, 'Do you, my dauty, say so?'

'I never heard,' she answered, somewhat gaily, seeing I was dumfoundered, 'that Job was a provision-merchant, or I would have an excuse for his wife's railing, having such a husband; but not to say too much about it, what do you think of letting it be known you intend to offer yourself in the room of Sheriff Stew?'

'Me!' cried I, in a consternation – 'I would as soon think of evening myself to a kenna-what.'

'And, why not?' was her sober quest; 'surely ye might be that. You know, you know, my dear Plack, that we are not now as we were.'

Then, after some more ambulation, she told me what had been the purpose of the deputation in the forenoon, advising me to consent to the proposal. But I told her that, although I maybe had a bit sleight at turning the penny, it was far from my hand and capacity to be a sheriff, whose duty it is to see rogues stretched, 'which,' quo' I 'it is weel known, is a most kittle part to play weel.'

'Nay,' said she, 'but you are not the first that did not know his genius before it was tried. As for the trouble, a tureen of turtle soup might be either a sheriff or an alderman. No, no, Plack; leave the matter to me – first sheriff, then alderman – and afterwards I know who will be Lady Mayoress;' in saying which, she gave me such a bewitching look, that I could not but keckle. So it came soon to a bearing, that I was to come forward; and, in the course of the evening, Deputy Spice, the grocer, was sent for to know particulars.

Deputy Spice was not at home, and Mrs Plack was frightened when she heard it; but he had gone to nugger mugger with some other person. But, while she was in the middle of her dolorosity anent this suspecting, he came to the door, and with him another of the common council, that had not been of the morning party, which shewed I was growing popular.

Hearing what was come to pass, Mrs Plack went away, leaving us to our ain confabble; and then we had all the outs and ins laid open. But just in the crisis of our discourse, there arose a shriek and a blast your eyes in the lobby, which took us all to the room door, when we beheld Mrs Plack lying on the floor, as it were in a cold swoon, and Jacob, the footman, limping as if his leg was put out of joint.

It seems that she had, somehow, not being used to it, put out the lamp in trying to snuff it, and Jacob, soon after, coming up in the dark, stumbled against her at the room door, by which arose all the hobbleshow. She, however, utterly denied, even to me, that she was in a listening posture at the keyhole.

Not, however, to spin out particulars till they grow tedious, when peace was restored, I consented to let the gentlemen think I was not sweert against being a sheriff, which made them both most content; and, thus, next morning, it was bruited about that I was to be the new one; so, in process of time, on the appointed day, I was chosen; to the great contentation of Mrs Plack, who was maybe more vogie of the honour than me. No that I was just heart-broken with the thought of being a sheriff of London, whilk is a higher post in the government than the Lord Provost of a city that shall be nameless.

Letter XVIII

But, although I say it that should not, having been myself one, the trade of magistrating is not one of great profit. There is no telling the outlay Mrs Plack was at, to pave the way, as she said, with splendid expectations of what would be our mayorality; 'deed, a dignity is not the ways and means to make a fortune. There was, however, an outcoming in being a sheriff, which I did not foresee so clearly as my wife. In short, it behoved us to be more circumspect in who we entertained in our house; no that we were by nature overly given to gavalling, for I did not like that way of life, and Mrs Plack made a conformity. Public stations, however, must be kept up; and there is a moral obligation on every titled citizen of London and elsewhere, to have a spit and raxes, to say nothing of a gawsy kail-pot and a winsome fish kettle – all which Mrs Plack provided of a prime quality. 'Deed, many more preed our trenchers than the flies.

At first we were lovish enough; and, thinking so, I spoke quietly anent the same to the wife, which set her on making a selection, shewing in it her wonted discretion; for she made no change till the year of my sheriffdom was out. Then, however, she was so scomfished by galravitching, that we went to a watering place; from which, when we returned, we lived a douce life, seeing only a few particular friends now and then; so that, by the time I was leeted to be an alderman – for a vacancy soon happened in the court into which I was chosen – we had the ball at our foot, and played it in a most genteel manner; which causes me here to make a notandum. Surely those ancestors were long-headed folk, by whom our glorious Constitution and Protestant ascendancy was framed, to obligate a man to be a sheriff before he comes to be an alderman, and an alderman before he is Lord Mayor. For sheriffs, being nearer to the commonality than aldermen, are more furthy among all classes – elbowing in slily with the gentry. Then, after having served, they can be most judiciously so fatigued, as to long for retirement, in which they need only visit and receive their betters. By the time they rise to be aldermen, it would be very extraordinary if they had not made a chioce circle of friends, to garnish their mayorality. After their mayorality, they naturally come, you know, to be among the great, and may do as they please, if they can afford it.

This I say here, that you may understand me as I go along; for if the arcana were not explained, it would not be easy for you to think, how, after my sheriffry, I came to pass so lowne a time, or how, when made an alderman, I was accounted one of the select – I might say the elect – only I do not like to construe that word to a profanation. The sheriffry is, indeed, a kind of purefaction, a leave-taking, or payway, given to the citizens in general; but an alderman enjoys a higher station of life, and a Lord Mayor is a real dignity. Aldermen who have passed the chair are no less, in my opinion, than a wee sort of nobility for the remainder of all their days.

Letter XIX

Anent my savoury mayorality, which came to pass four years after I had been made an alderman, it becomes not me to speak, especially as it may be read of in the newspapers of that victorious year. And, by all accounts, it will be no edification to you, Geordie, to read of it; for maybe it would instigate you to buy a third gelding, and ask for another replenishment; so I will go on to talk of doucer matters.

Being, you see, the father but of a dochter, your mother, it did not consort with my notions to lay out money for a vanity, as I count certain kind of epitaphs to be; and, therefore, when it was said to me, after I had been Lord Mayor, that I might be a Bawronet, I eschewed it, because it was not an inheritance which I could bequeath to Mary, that was ordained to be the heiress to my bit gathering; accordingly, I was most obstinatious on the point. I'll no deny that, maybe, had there been a male get in the case, I would have seen things in another light, and both bought a pretty estate in the country, and a bawronetcy forbye, to transmit my name to the latest posterity. That, however, not being ordained in the councils of wisdom, it behoved me to look at baith sides of the bawbee before I wared it, and I made up my mind not to faik a farthing for such a balloon matter as a teetle – not, I am sure, that, after having served mayor, it would have cost me much more than the fees; but the fees were a penny, and I have aye thought that a penny hained is a penny gained. In fact, I'll no say that a bawronetcy, got for doing weel in the magisterial line, is just a disgrace to any man; and it's surely far better than laying out thousands for sic like, as certain country gentlemen have done, who I know, with high heads; but they, poor feathers, shall be nameless. Howsomever, a bawronet I would not be, for I thought it a concos mentos job to pay for a nickname; as I told Mrs Plack a bawronetcy surely, though of a genteel kind, was. She said precious little, and I never let on that I saw her glunching and glooming with the tail of my ee; but being rather of a kindly nature – as you know I am, Geordie, or ye would never ask me for a replenishment – I grew wae to observe the effect, for she waxed wan and dowie, and became greatly given to yawning, which the auld proverb notified to me was a bad sign –

Them that gaunt, something want –
Sleep, meat, or making o'.

And, being fashed thereat, I said to her in bed, on a Sunday morning, when she had reason to be well pleased, that I was of opinion that she would not be the worse of a jaunt somewhere in the warm month. 'Indeed,' quo' she, 'I have had a notion of that myself.' So out of this rose that great come-to-pass which led us to forgether with your lordly faither, then in a straitened circumstance; but of the particulars I shall speak in my next. So no more at present. – Yours, &c.

Letter XX

But, before I tell of our jaunt, it is needful to relate a few particulars that came to pass ere we set out.

When our dochter had been five years under the wing of that most discreet woman, Mrs Mortimer, and had learnt more than I can tell, it behoved us to bring her home.

By this time she wasna an ill-faurt lassie – as comely as a red cheekit apple, my wife would say; but she was a thought given to outing when onything pleased her. Indeed, with Mrs Mortimer's connivance, to say the least o't, Clemy had grown a credit baith to the school and her parents likewise.

She came home at the Midsummer holidays; and it was proposed, as she could not be 'brought out' till the winter, that, in the meantime, we should take the jaunt to let her see the world, and particularly that part of it which is in Great Britain called Scotland. Against this I was not sweert; for Scotland, ye ken, was my calf-country, and I had an inclination to go to Glasgow and see if it was as pleasant as ever; for I minded the blinks of daffiing I had when in it a poor barefooted laddie, and I aye thought that surely it was a land of much blessedness – that scant and want could in it be almost heartsome. So it was agreed, towards the latter end of July, that we should set out, and travel easy, hoping the weather would be fine, with an elderly woman on the dickey with the footman. The woman was well recommended to us as a sedate motherly character, with an experience that my wife would find most useful in inns and places where a lightheaded maiden would need looking after.

I was the more consenting to hire Mrs Snod, because she was a Scotch woman born, and could 'terpret for us in the language of that country, my long residenting in London having naturally made me no to understand it aff hand, or to speak it without an accent. To tell the truth, this consideration anent the tongue had its weight for some time with me, and I could not make up my mind, by reason of it, to go all the way to Scotland, till that god-send, Mrs Snod, made me set a stout heart to a stey brae.

But, although I had my own prudente about going to the northerly land of Canaan, I'll no take it upon me to deny that I had now a wish to go thither; for I had a very strong wish. Indeed, everybody kens that it is as natural for a Scotchman, who has done well in the world, to shew his testimonies among his kith and kin when he grows old, as it is for him to eat parritch for his breakfast, and to go about barefooted when young, especially those that have been of my degree. So having, by reason of Mrs Snod, gotten the whip-hand of difficulty, we set out, as I have said; and here it becomes me, my man Geordie, to make an improvement for your behoof.

Having, as you have seen, raised myself by my own merit and geny into maybe a bein way of life, there could be no solid obstacle to my shewing I could come in my own carriage among my auld friends; and so I let my wife understand; saying that I would put on no sauce, but go among them with a blithe guid-day here, and a couthy good-e'en there; therefore it behoved her to make agreeable faces, to shew we both could carry a full cup. Clemy, our dochter, I did not think it was inevitable to instruct; for she was a real fine thing, mim as a rose-bud and sweet as a plum, and had mair politess and pleasantry in her wee finger than baith her parents had in their whole bouks. This your mother, however, would not allow, and therefore I have no need to flatter her to cause you to love her; but she was, if I may say it, in my eyes a golden creature, in so much that a minister of the gospel, whom I fell in with in Scotland, where they much abound, said of her to me, that her gentleness and modesty certified to him that her parents lived according to the evangelists – nor did I gainsay him; but I may tell you, for ye have a kind of an e'e in your neck, ye sorrow, that now and then I thought her mother was a wee condumacious, which is the original sin of all wives, especially when they are in the right – that, however, thanks and be praise! they very seldom are, or there would be no living with them.

Letter XXI

But now to begin about the jaunt. When a' thing was put in an order, me and the guidwife, your grannie, with Clemy, your lady mother, after an early breakfast, steppit into our own carriage, whereto, behind, divers trunks were strappit; and we trintlet awa down the north road, taking the airt of the south wind that blaws in Scotland. At first it was very pleasant; and as I had never been much in the country in a chaise, I was diverted to see how, in a sense, the trees came to meet us, and passed, as if they had been men of business having a turn to do.

After various observes anent this comical movement, a sleepy thought came over me; and the guidwife, who was fain to be a leddy-ship, not being in a talkative inclination, I lay back in the chaise, and had a most conneck and comfortable visitation to the land of nod for some time; in so much that, when we came to an inns where it behoved us to take a pause, I was as fresh as a newly shelled pea, and felt an admonishment I had an appety; so we made there a consolatory dinner, the mistress being well pleased with the cold lamb and the lettuses, which she judiciously said was as cool as cucumber.

After our solatium at 'The Frightened Mouse,' which was the name of the arms, finding a long evening before us, we took a dish of tea, and bidding the coachman get his horses ready, renewed our jaunting; and, at a reasonable hour, about nine o'clock in the gloaming, alighted in another public, where they sold strong ale that was just a cordial; which, to tell no lees, put such smeddum intil me that I was heartened to go a stage farther. Lucky it was that I did so and I was so courageous; for it was a far better house, and in it there was everything to be had that the heart of man could have a notion of.

We passed a pleasant night; but I was a thought troubled with the nocturnals, by reason of the strong ale of the predecessing public.

The day thereafter was more of a moderation in all things; we journeyed on with a sobriety that was heartsome without banter; for really the parks on both sides of the road were salutary to see. The hay was mown, and the corn was verging to the yellow. The haws on the hedges, though as green as capers, were a to-look; the cherries in the gardens were over and gone; but the apples in the orchards were as damsels entering their teens.

When I was nota-beneing in this way, your grandmother consternated a great deal to Clemy, saying she never thought that I had such a beautiful taste for the poeticals, and that I was surely in a fit of the bucolicks. But I, hearing her, told her I had aye a notion of the country; only that I had soon seen fallen leaves were not coined money, which, if a man would gather, it behoved him to make his dwelling-place in the howffs and thoroughfares of the children of men.

This led us on to a very conjugal crack, which, with the lowne influence of the air, led us into what may be called paths of pleasantness; in so much that the guidwife said it was a sore pity my geny had not been cultivated, for that I had surely a nerve.

This commendation of my parts from her drew me into a confabble concerning divers matters which I had noticed in my life; and I told her I had seen that all great men of my kything were just wanton when they could stretch their tethers and gambol in the country, the reason whereof I could not tell; but it was a proof that the stoury minds of town folk, and of those who sit maundering in offices, have only their vocations, as it were, in cages, and ken not the beatin in the breasts of the birds that make blithesome the boughs.

It is indeed a jocose remembrance to think, in my auld age, of that jaunt and the pleasant day thereof – the primest, I may say, till then, of my life; for, till then, though I had been in a sense a thriving man, there was yet, maybe, now and then a seasoning of fashery in my lot.

Thus it came to pass, in the course of the second day after we set out on our journey, which we intended to be for only a fortnight, that we came to a resolution to make a desultory job of it, and to go hither and yon, if the weather was good, as might seem comely to ourselves; and so, when we stopped for the night, I wrote to my head clerk and told him no to trouble me with anything pertaining to the lucre of gain till he heard of my return to the earth; likening London to that region, and the scope of our journey as a tea-drinking visit to Adam and Eve, naked in a state of innocence, in the garden of Eden.

It was in this way, coming afield, and having nothing to do, that we made sport and pleasantry to ourselves; the upshot of which, as I have already let wit, was the matteromonial connection of your father, that was born a lord, with my only dochter, whereof I shall speak by and by. In the meantime, let me rehearse the uncos we fell in with.

Letter XXII

At this distance of time, I cannot undertake to say that all our carouse along the king's highway was alike pleasant. We had no doubt our own ups and downs, to say nothing of showery days, and cod fish of the sea that were very high in inland towns; but of a certainty we did not stint ourselves in feasting on the fat of the land, going to the right and to the left, with sundry sojourns in good inns; the which, in my solid opinion, make it an obligation for a man well to do to take sometimes the door on his back, the staff in his hand, and speer the way to the well at the world's end. In truth, that jaunt gave me both pleasantry and insight; for I soon discovered how it happens that men who wax bien, and are yet neither rich enough nor sufficiently upsetting to be made magistrates, are so given in the summer time to jaunting. They dinna very well know, nor their wives likewise, how to keep companies at home; but having the natural longing for flesh pots that all those in a state of prosperity have, they surely have a right to gratify themselves by going to and fro like roaring lions, seeking where they may devour. But not to digress about them, it's just necessar that I should give a bit inkling on the matter, to let you see that I make observes; for it was by so doing that I found out the reason of genteel jaunts in po'-chaises, when shadows are short and days are long, by decent folk that live soberly at home. Having done so, I will touch on them no more, but resume our charioteering.

Having resolved, as I have said, that, for a while, because we could afford it, we should take our foot in our hand, we told the coachman that we would trust ourselves to him and Providence, so that he was free to go where he pleased, and take us to any place that he thought would entertain us, and we see uncos; so being thus 'mancipated, he drove us to a town which we knew could not but be to the right, for the sun which had hitherto been on our backs, came to our left, and was, by course of nature, in our e'en before setting – a certain demonstration.

However, there was a Providence in our going thither; for at the house where we put up, Mrs Plack had a confabble with the landlady in secret, who told her that we were not far, not more than a stage, from Addleborough; which caused us to make a deviation, for good and substantial reasons best known to ourselves, respecting which I will let you into the secret in my next. Be ye, therefore, content with this curt letter till then. Patience is a fine thing for a young man to learn, being, in a certain sense, better than all the lear of Oxford, whereof no deacon of men is a worshipper unless he thinks of making his bread by the wind of his mouth.

Letter XXIII

When my wife heard we were so near Addleborough, she remembered a cousin, who was married and settled in that town, with a merchant for her guidman, and said it would be friendly to give her a call; so we went there, never thinking of staying aboon ae night. But the ways of nature are most mystical; we staid the best half of a whole week, so weel pleased were we with our cousin and her acquaintances, for they were all the topping of the town. It would be too tedious to mention them by name; but one of them was a great litterally character, who sent into the newspapers every month something about the tides and changes of the moon, with other lunaticals most kittle to understand, and had, moreover, on the outside of his bedroom window, a weather glass, screwed up in a 'stronomy manner, perplexing to ordinary folk, wherewith he held a secret wark; for all that, however, he was a genteel man, and no without commonsense, knowing something of Christianity in a degree.

But, Geordie, it may not be plain to you, though I dinna despair of your understanding, what good it could do to me to be with philosophers. Howsomever, I'll tell you.

You know that, in my beginning, I did not cleave to riches, but as a means; mind that – as a means. I saw that the rich commanded the earth; and I thought if I could get near unto riches, I could not be far off from every other thing; and so to get near to them was all my ettle. But, as I began to get up, sidy for sidy with them, I got an inkling that there was the use of riches needful to be learnt, as well as the way to get them, and that in striving for them, I had thought too earnestly only of them. I missed use altogether; in so much, when my hogger was of a condition to bide being shaken in the teeth of the wind, I was no quite sure how best to lay out my talent to the usury, which is real profit. I am now speaking seriously; so give ear attentively.

The first of this suspicion I had during our sojourn at Addleborough. Hitherto in London – with my bit jobs on the Stock Exchange, melting of bills in a canny way, and with one thing and another – my hands were held full and thrang, so that I had no leisure to make *nota benes* about mankind; but, at Addleborough, though we bided there but four days, my eyes were opened, and I saw it was not enough to make money – that was not difficult with God's blessing, though men that can only make money, think muckle of the talon, and have a notion that those upon the thrive have great merit; but to know what to do with money is the craft of life. Many, no doubt, make a sight of money by hook and by crook, and think they thereby do well; but I do not think so of them, being in all things of the notion, that honesty is the best politicks; having noticed, at the mention of some rich men's names, that decent folk wag their heads with a scrupulosity.

Among hands with our gavalling at Addleborough, I had leisure enough to have justified me in thinking long; and had I no been one that had ever a turn to do, surely the time in the forenoons would have gone dreichly; but while my wife was confabbing, anent this and that, with her cousin, I went about the doors, spying the nakedness of the land; by which I soon saw that a borough's town was not the New Jerusalem for me, though maybe it's no unlike that city which, is said, in the Psalms of David, to be compactly built together; in short, all in a borough's town strive for themselves, whereas in the metropolis, some work for the public. No that in a sense that's neglected in provincials either; but there the vista of advantage shews the recompense nigher at hand for what is done, than in the capital, by which maybe a disinterestedness is seemingly caused – I say seemingly, for I am no sure, after all, that men are egged by better feelings in London than elsewhere; though sure and certain it is, that there are men in the metropolis that are actuated by other look-tos than folks, decent though they be, in a country town.

Letter XXIV

Having surfeited ourselves with Addleborough, me and Mrs Plack had one morning in bed a great controversy about what we should do next. I was for going right on to Glasgow; but she would not hear of such a thing, being intent to see Edinburgh, and especially the writers and poets there, whom she said were, to a moral certainty, the primest, according to their own opinion, in the whole 'versal world; putting out books in shoals and nations, and making such to do, with a Review, whether of soldiers or cavalry I know not, that was fearsome to hear; so, in the end, to keep peace in the house, I was obligated to make a capitulation, the upshot of which was, that, leaving Addleborough, away we came to Edinburgh; which, after divers pleasing inspections of curiosities, we reached by the end of the week, and tabernacled in the Royal Hotel, where all thing is very orderly.

It is not to be contested that Edinburgh has a certain similitude to London; for, if the one has the tower, the other has a castle; and provice, it is well known, is just the Scottish word for mayor, as it is the proper English to call a bailie an alderman. Upon the whole, Edinburgh, although this was the first time I had seen it, is not quite as big as London; but well does every Scotchman ken that is is a most fine place; if there should be a doubt that in greatness, it's no just a match for the metropolis.

But, Geordie, a word in your lug, and let it go no farther: yon is a very cold place, especially when the wind is easterly; and all the merchants thereof, together with the rest that make money, are in the main, shopkeepers. As for the writers, I was just confounded; we have nothing like them in London. Poets there are no better than stacks of duds; but in Edinburgh, man, if ye forgathered with some of them, they would gar you believe that spade-shafts would bear plumbs.

One piece of wastry I noticed in Edinburgh – if it be wastry to be negligent, but it no doubt comes of their gentility – and that is in their state of the streets, in that blaw-thorough, their new town. The streets there are most dreadful, having on them the very finest grass sward that can be, whereupon a whole flock of sheep might fatten, to say nothing of black cattle. Really yon is a shame, especially when, in the country, commons, as I heard, are everywhere on the diminution. I think the 'conomists of Edinburgh would shew gumption, if they had but geese on yon commons. I was told, however, that those quadrupeds were not liked there, because the Edinburghers are not cannibals, fond of eating their own speshy. However, it does not do to be overly particular about the causes of anything, when, like me, a man sees but as it were a blink. So, to make an end, I got my wife, your grandmother, in three days, to leave yon cauldrife similarity to a city, and to come to Glasgow, which is a town – as everybody knows, who has ever been within the four corners of it, and at the Broomielaw – where the load coals in gabbarts, with other manufactures, too tedious to mention. It behoves me, however, to be a little more on the sprose with Glasgow; it being the place where I first set up in business, as I have already rehearsed to you.

Letter XXV

Glasgow was mair to my liking than Edinburgh, for the people there are all in a stir, which gladdens me to see. Only, they are greatly given to coomy work and have an overplush of foul lums and steam engines. Still they are braw, hearty, and ettling; and have, as the sailors say, 'the weather-gauge' of the poor thread-papers of a town that's easterly.

Everybody in Glasgow is busy making money in the best way he can; nor is he looked down upon that thrives, though he may not be topping. This is kent by them all; and there is nae rifting in a neighbour's face, when they have gotten a fu' kite. But they are no without a sense of difference, though they dinna account a dealer in cauk and herrings by retail a merchant, as they do in Edinburgh. For a' that, however, it cannot be said, in justice, that they are void of upsetting; and now and then, it must be allowed that one perishes the pack among them without bigging of kirks, though they do manufacture kirks there, and it's a thriving branch of business. On the whole, they are an eident people, and maybe there is some hidden way of thrift in their outing; but our stay was not what we intended, and we were, in a manner, constrained suddenly to turn our faces to the southard; the reason whereof is this: –

Ye'll mind John Douce and his wife, whereof, about my outset I made mention. Well, by this time, with God's blessing, and his wife's council, John had thriven into a bailieship; and, as they were the first folk after our arrival that I went to see, they were just out of the body, and nothing would serve them, as I had been a Lord Mayor, and was rich, as some said, than that we should all bide with them; which, to say the truth, was like forcing us to put on pumps of a narrow capacity. However, as they would take no denial, especially the mistress, we were obligated to go to their house. Long did we rue that rash action.

John Douce, as I have said, being high on the tree, could not be complaisant enough; accordingly, as lang as we continued to stay in the royal city, he resolved, because I had been a Lord Mayor, to have all the big wigs of the town, with the Principal and Professors of the College, to see what would come out after his long corks were drawn. And thus it came to pass, that, day after day, we had a banqueting at his house.

At first, nothing could go off grander; and it was a visibility to me, who knew something of the auld, that the bailie's wife had, every night, no been blate with her curtain lectures, which partly accounted for the heck-and-manger treatment that we received. Every day, for example, we had a brave cut of a fresh salmon, boiled with the scales no taken off, which Mrs Douce, at the head of the table, shoveled about, as if to shew how well-used she was to the dividing. But, no to be particular, I should here make mention that this daily cut-and-come-again of the salmon was a ministering means of our sudden evasion from the het and fu' roof of Bailie Douce's; and, as we could not, in a sense, go from it to an inn, we made a *parley-vous* departure from Glasgow.

Now, you'll be licking your lips, Geordie, to hear how a very nice cut of salmon at Glasgow could be a cause of a London alderman to eschew that corpulent city; and, for an edification, I will tell you.

It was not because we had it every day, but because we once had it not as it ought to have been. The particulars whereof are surely most comical, as I shall presently rehearse – not, however, so much for an instruction as for an entertainment, and as a touch-and-go hint that ye may turn to profit when ye have a house of your ain; for, mind, though ye may be a Lord's son, the French anarchy and confusion at Parish has taught us that to siclike Miss Fortune has long arms and heavy hands, longer than kings' – and theirs, we all know, are not short; nor are ye ayont her reach – the cankry old maiden.

Had the whereof anent the cut of salmon come to pass in these Radical times, it would have been no unco; but to happen when the bailies of Glasgow were drinking their cool punch, every one under his vine and fig-tree, was surely judgment-like – and the rough of it is this: Mrs Douce had ordained, that every day we stayed with them, as Leven salmon were then very nice, we should have a cut at dinner, fresh and fresh; and every day there was somebody at the table just out of the body with the fish, especially when they held out their trencher for a second sample, saying how fine it was. Thus it came to pass, by the Saturday, that the bailie was very vogie to think of the renown he would acquire for his most excellent fat Leven salmon.

But when Saturday came, there was a catastrophe.

The weather, it being the eye of summer, was very warm, which everybody knows is not salutary for keeping of salmon, especially when they have to be brought in an open cart from Dumbarton in the sun; in consequence, when the bailie's serving lass, with her bare feet and her red arms, went with a basket to buy a salmon, all that were in the market were high, and if she had not taken one of them she would have gotten none; so it happened that she brought home a salmon that the bailie said, when he smelt it at dinner, was surely in a bad way. A professor of the College, however, sitting by, told him that the fish was not to blame, had it been rightly cooked; but 'the Devil sends cooks,' &c.

John Douce (I mean the bailie) heard all but said nothing; only, as the salmon smelt like Billingsgate in the dog days, as Mr Deputy Creesh, the tallow-chandler used to say of high fish, it was sent away from the table. However, at night, when the company broke up, the bailie went frying with passion into the kitchen, and an angry man was he at the lass for no boiling the salmon in a christian-like manner; the which word nettled madam, and she gave him a salt answer, really so provoking that he could no do better than nip her arm with very little loving kindness, insomuch that, on the Sabbath morning, next day, she could not be found.

Once away and aye away. She was gallanting with a clerk, who put her up to summons her master, the bailie, on the Monday, afore the Court, where she shewed the stends of the nip, black and blue; and he was glad to compound for no small sum; which so soured his temper, that me and my wife consulted in conclave about taking the door on our backs; – indeed, we were tired of travelling and wished to be at home again. To have gone instanter would not, however, have been well-bred for folks in our station of life; so we covenanted to say we were going to Cheltenham to drink the physic water with Clemy, and really could bide no longer; and, to make no breach of the truth, we resolved to go straight thither, as fast as many wheels could take us, for we both hated to the uttermost detestation not to keep our words.

Having bade adieu to Glasgow, we set out betimes in the morning, and taking the canny town of Paisley in our way, we breakfasted there, and syne gaed up and down the streets, for it was a fine day. Afterwards an accident befell us most comical to hear; for, among the other manufactories, Mrs Plack, your grandmother heard the Paisley bodies were famous for making dressing, and she resolved that her and Clemy should have a gown of it. But, och hone, poor Lucky! When we came to send for a swatch, saying we just wanted to see it, they sent us a cog of sowans – dressing being but the reform name of sowans; for I knew them again, as such, outright, when I saw them.

From Paisley we went to Kilmarnock, which is a town, but what it is remarkable for I do not know; only I remember in the days of my youth they made orthoxies there, and shoes of all denominations.

We then went to Ayr, where we had a chack of dinner, and were minded to have gone farther that night; but, being out of Glasgow, we thought better o't, and staid there, not leaving it till the morn's morning, for it is a genty place, and well worth an investigation; only the eggs in it are not cordials, as we found at breakfast, for I tried three of them, and they were the progeny of a hen that surely had a complaint, and were a main cause of our hurrying on to Cheltenham; for they were dreadful.

Letter XXVII

Cheltenham is a most fine place; and there it was that we forgethered with my Lord, your father – a decent well-behaved lad, but sorely pinched.

It happened that we put up at the 'Plough Inn,' where he was biding; and, the morning after our arrival there, when I had gotten my breakfast, I went down to the coffeeroom, before me and the wife would go out with Clemy, to see the bill of fare, in which I saw there was to be a roasted lion, with sweet sauce, for dinner.

'Bless my soul!' quo' I to the waiter, 'can that be a true lion?' – whereupon your father, who was sitting in a box hard by, rose and told me, with a pleasant smile, in a very couthy manner for a lord to do, that it was only a hare which had been shot by a ne'er-do-weel poacher; and from that time we sidled into acquaintance, till, from less to more, I invited him to take a cut of the lion with us, which was the cause of your being born upon earth, and may be the reason how you came to write to me for a replenishment.

After this introduction, I soon could see, by the e'e in my neck, that the young lord was casting a sheep's eye at our Clemy, who came, in time, to be her ladyship, your lawful mother. At first, for a convenient season, I had no broo of this; for I have aye had a notion that lords were a kind of canary-headed cattle, having, for the most part, a want; but, in the end, I was in a sense constrained, by your granny's exhortations, to make myself no unreasonable; so, at length, I consented to covenant that I should shell out my bodles for an inducement; so, without summering and wintering more, the upshot was, that your father espoused my dochter, with five and twenty thousands of pounds, and wadsets, as it may be called, of twice as mickle more, at my becoming functy offishy, which is the law for departing this life in a Christian way.

Your father being, by course of his father's extravagance – which was awful – a needful lord, was thus set up among the nobility in a genteel way, especially by his to-look at me; and I having earned, by my ettling, all that it was ever in my wish to do, thought it was but right to enjoy the outcomings of the merits of my talons.

By and by, when ye came to be a most provoking plague, I had you for a pastime; which I jealouse is the cause ye tell me that horses have yawp appeties, and that grumes are eating moths at the college of Oxford.

Howsomever, ca' canny, my lad, Geordie; for ye see that, if I had not been a man of discretion, I, who was not come of a pedigree, never could have been in a way to write for a replenishment. In short, take tent, and eschew racing cattle, and ponder well the o'ercome of my experience, making your home by the chumla lug, and going to the kirk on the Lord's Day.

But, Geordie, no to be overly on you, I will now make an end; and maybe ye'll find in the corner enclosed a bit slip of paper, with the which, and what I have said, trusting you will never rax your arm farther than your sleeve will let you, I subscribe myself your loving gotchard,

Archibald Plack.

THE STATESMAN

The Resignation

Having attained my grand climacteric, I deemed it expedient to think of retiring from public life, and, having caught a severe cold during a warm debate, I resolved on the execution of the measure long contemplated; especially when I saw by the division that our administration was losing ground. Men of less experience might not have so soon discerned the direction in which I clearly perceived the fabric was settling; but, through a long vista of notices of vexatious motions in perspective, I saw some change inevitable, and accordingly, as the doctor was of opinion that I should abstain from the irritations of business, I secluded myself from the world.

For two days I was unequivocally indisposed, and one of the treasury journals had a sympathetic paragraph on the effects which my patriotic anxieties respecting the issue of the question had produced on a constitution not naturally robust, and whose stamina indefatigable application had tended not to improve. It was, therefore, not altogether on the responsibility of my own understanding that I acted; for I am free to confess, that the feeling insinuation had some influence in the advent of that conclusion to which I had come.

It has happened, that although the course of coercive medicine which I pursued, had on the third day induced convalescence, and made it decidedly obvious, yet such had been the impression produced upon me by the manifest unstable state of his majesty's then existing government, that a diplomatic augmentation of all the deleterious symptoms of my catarrh was permitted to assume the ascendency. In a word, I saw myself in a crisis of life and office that no longer allowed me to blink the intention of resignation. Accordingly, on the fifth day subsequent to the grievous consideration, I laid all my trusts at the feet of a royal and most gracious master.

The Letter, and its Consequences

The letter in which I took this final and important step was much commended by my colleagues, but it was not necessary to make them acquainted with its private history; which, however, was as follows: –

Being confined to my room, I directed my private secretary, who had been senior wrangler at Cambridge, and who wrote a very superior style, to prepare a suitable letter; in which, justly comprehending what was required, he made a faithful transcript of my sentiments, which I signed at once, and handed it back to be made up.

My emotion, however, at the time, betrayed itself; the letter fell from my hand; the young gentleman stooped to pick it up. By some unaccountable accident, at the same moment the standish was overset, and the ink, flowing on the floor, obliterated the writing.

The letter was thus rendered nugatory; but I calmly requested my secretary not to be disturbed, saying, as he had much to do, I would myself make a copy. Thus my resignation was a holograph; and several of the ministerial papers afterwards noticed the circumstance, and highly commended its excellence.

For some time – indeed, for a long time – immediately subsequent to my resignation, habits of official assiduity made the winged hours, as the poet says, bestow on me their tediousness. I saw, however, the clouds thicken, and the eclipse coming on, of which the prognostications were so legible, and could not but congratulate myself on the prudence by which I had so been induced to resign. I retired from the storm, and resolved, in the hereditary towers of my family-castle, which I had not visited for many years – not since the county was last contested – to enjoy the evening of life in serenity – *otium cum dignitate.*

Accordingly, with that decision and promptitude to which, in public transactions, I owe so much, I stepped into my travelling carriage; and in the words of a great cardinal, bade 'a long farewell to all my greatness,' quitting the metropolis by the North Road.

The Journey

During the first stage, my thoughts were all adrift; restless as the whipper-in of the House of Commons, when a debate on an important ministerial motion 'looks d – d queer,' and the opposition leader on his legs is unanswerable.

But as we went down into the country, 'the smell of dairy,' as the inimitable Shakespeare calls it, began to harmonise my spirits; insomuch, that by the time we reached the summit of St. Alban's hill I could say, with the philosophic orator of antiquity, 'How stale, flat, and unprofitable, are all the offices of this weary world!' A reflection, to one retiring to the embraces of innocent nature, most conducive to the bosom's tranquillity.

In the fourth stage, at the end of which I proposed to ruminate in the inn after dinner, I felt moral tendencies of a salutary kind, and called to mind that I might yet serve my king and country, by explaining in my retirement some of those maxims which contribute so much to the prosperity of nations and the celebrity of statesmen.

At no period of my eventful career, indeed, had I squared my conduct with reference to the narrow-minded remark of the Danish minister who observed to his son, 'How little sagacity was requisite for the rule of kingdoms!' My own experience inculcated a different lesson; for, when the spirit of the age ran strong against men in high stations, I often thought the *vox populi* was the *vox Dei*, and stood in awe of anarchy and confusion.

Thus it came to be determined, before I reached the feudal magnificence of Verbose Castle, that I should devote the evening twilight of life to the composition of a treatise on the principles by which states may be ruled best, and statesmen justly appreciated in the estimates of all men. The result is embodied in the following pages.

Parliament

A man destined by hereditary circumstances generally completes his education at one of the universities, in order that he may there acquire a competent knowledge of the names of the classics, and something of that learning, more essential to the business of afterlife, which can only be obtained by attending the social nocturnal lucubrations so well established there.

In process of time, young and enterprising, just come of age, and all his faculties redolent with vigour, he takes his place in the great council of the nation; in which, for so many ages, understandings undebauched by experience have been so requisite to withstand the fatigue of midnight deliberation.

I, therefore, devote the dogmas of my instructions to explain the energies of those duties which should be paramount to all others at this interesting period.

If the future minister be of a certain rank, he is generally selected by the manager of the House of Commons to play a part in which he may become distinguished: for this purpose, he is commonly chosen to move the address consequent on the speech from the throne; and for two reasons; first, that he may not be overwhelmed by his innate diffidence at hearing better orators before him; and, second, by having only a speech to recite, he may not have occasion to answer any impertinent remark. All is arranged in the most agreeable manner, and every thing done that can mitigate any apprehension which may be entertained for him among his friends, on the score of capacity or the scope of talent.

In the early periods of my arduous life, men confined themselves to the dry business before the house; but when I came to see the dangers in affairs of government of being too plain and downright, I endeavoured what in me lay to effect a reformation in the character of debates. I accordingly advised the young and new members, especially those whom I thought, by the structure of their oral sentences, to be desirous of distinction as orators, to provide themselves with a dictionary of quotations, and, whenever they intended to have a field-day, to pick out of it some pithy apophthegm; at the same time telling them, that in this matter there was no need to be very particular, for that the country gentlemen, who are very fond of hearing Latin, did no much care about the meaning of the words, and that the public considered they must skip it in the newspapers. 'It is, however,' said I, 'becoming a gentleman who is desirous of being thought accomplished.' Thus, in process of time, Horace was as well known in the house as any political potentate; and poets rose into celebrity. But, although the use of quotations tends to elevate the eloquence of ambitious speakers, yet those who had scruples respecting the accuracy of their classical pronunciation I counselled to addict themselves to the public accounts.

I remember well a friend saying facetiously on the subject, 'That embryo chancellors of the exchequer were as plentiful as blackberries.' At which *bon mot* we both laughed very heartily.

I observed, at the opening of every new parliament, that the scions of aristocracy did not introduce, so often as they might have done, Latin sentences into their speeches: it was, indeed, a long time before the custom was established. They stood in awe of the merchants and men of business; but, nevertheless, men in office were ready with applauses: for, we had observed, the judicious world is prepared to distinguish employed ability.

After scrutinising the four parliaments in which I sat with the Commons during my father's life, I came to the conclusion that he is not ordained to be a rising man who confines himself to great questions only; and, in consequence, I recommended to those who wished to make themselves conspicuous to attend to petitions.

'Get a petition,' said I, 'from the inhabitants of some well-known and satisfactory town; make yourself acquainted, if you can, with the grievance it sets forth; and, when the benches are empty, and the reporters can hear every word, get up close to the Speaker – mind that! – and, holding forth in his ear to the utmost of your ability, you will be sure to see what you have said in the papers next morning. That is the way to thrive in popularity, which leads to places and pensions. I could name many senators, now of great notoriety, who began modestly with unheard-of petitions – all for bringing in bills to repeal forgotten statutes – who have since risen into sinecures of emolument and patronage.'

It is, however, men of only a particular conformation of intellect that are calculated to acquire influence within the honourable house, by the presentation of petitions breathing sedition, or, in other words, discontent; for there is always a number of busy bodies who have a suspicion, and say it too, that the exaggerations of national grievances are got up by men in boroughs, not more conspicuous for thrift in their vocations than those who play the same *rôle* in parliament. But I was never much regarded as a petitionmonger; for my preceptor (who, in consequence of having been so, is now a bishop) was a sagacious man, who did not much venerate the local effusions of intellectual bile, and took particular pains to warn me of mixing myself up with them. He saw that I was destined, by my abilities, to fill the highest offices of the state, and therefore considered it of importance to adopt every precaution that might have the effect of preventing me from being seduced by popular demagogues. Nor was it in the matter of petitions alone that his discernment was efficacious; he was particularly careful to advise me never to attend ordinary committees – such as those on road and canal bills, and measures only advantageous to the plebeians of the kingdom; 'because men,' said he, 'who aspire to office, ought to make themselves valuable according to my Lord Lauderdale's definition of the term. No grandeur of character can be obtained by any man who places himself on a level with those who may have more accurate local information; and few statesmen, even out of office, have so little regard for their reputation as to allow themselves to be expected at private committees.'

There is a way, however, of obtaining distinction in the house, which I have myself observed, if the member be a country gentleman, or of no hereditary eminence, and does not attempt to make himself an impressive speaker; and it is frequently practised, though the precise rule for it is not clearly laid down; namely, to keep moving from seat to seat during the stillness of a solemn debate, and to look as if you had much to do, and secrets to whisper to many men. The effect of this mutability is astonishing; for, if a man gain nothing else, he makes himself personally known to the reporters, and his name becomes among them, and by them to the newspapers, as familiar as a household word.

In fact, while the British constitution is of a mixed nature, it is of the utmost consequence that public men should be celebrated for something: the man who moves about the house during the elocution of a much-attended-to orator, is supposed to have a world of important affairs on hand, especially if he make himself so annoying as to be called to order by Mr Speaker.

Under-Secretary of State

When a gentleman has acquired a competent knowledge of the House of Commons, and sees clearly the necessity of standing well with the reporters, and, of course, with the public, he is usually made an under-secretary of state. I therefore propose to give a few cursory recommendations, which may be useful to those who aim at that degree.

If the candidate for office be a man of talent, which some of them accidentally are, his native tact will enable him to discern what is necessary; but if he be himself only conscious of having inherited a peculiar endowment, then to a certainty he is inapt to derive wisdom from the lessons of experience. Men of talent are pretty much in the way of acting like ordinary persons; and this fact was amongst the earliest discoveries which I made of character when I entered public life, and it was not agreeable: for certainly it is a singular thing, that superior men differ so little from the commonalty of mankind, that kings often, under a belief of promoting ability by attending too much to eccentricities, raise incompetent individuals to offices of great importance; as witness, for example, my successor, who, notwithstanding in private life he is of the most unsullied purity of morals, endeavours to act to the best of his ability, which is any thing but great.

Those who think they are destined for the high offices of state, should make themselves remarkable; for if a man aspire to distinction, he will find it most conducive to that end to assume something odd and peculiar in his behaviour: because the commonalty of the world consider eccentricity as an indication of genius. Men of the world say, however, that it is a surer symptom of absurdity.

Under-secretaries of state are, for the most part, promising young men; not that they are more deceptive than other members of government, but there is a promise of future eminence among them which is often surprising. I would, therefore, advise all such aspirants as under-secretaries to be very guarded in interviews, and to take care not to practise those affable condescensions which may betray them to unveil their ignorance.

Sometimes it does happen, that, at interviews with deputations, under-secretaries meet with shrewd characters; and, therefore, it is highly expedient that they should not always appear very clearly informed of the business of the meeting. They should, therefore, say little; and their excuse for doing so should be a doubt of what their principals may think on the subject, after they shall have been informed of what has been so very ably urged and represented. In fact, an under-secretary of state should not be too candid; otherwise his principal would have no way of eliciting himself. And I need not observe, that it is quite as important to have it supposed that there is ability at the helm of affairs, as to do things well.

Another point is essential to be considered by under-secretaries of state. They are the inlets of the knowledge which should penetrate into the interior of cabinets, and they should, therefore, be very chary about what they allow to enter. They are, in fact, the rulers of the state, and their superiors but superintendents; which is the cause, no doubt, that young men, in the full vigour of life and prejudice, are preferred for the office. Cabinet ministers have something else to do – to say nothing of their dinners – than to discuss the issue of the measures upon which they are called to deliberate. It may, therefore, be owing to some occult device of policy that they select raw and inexperienced scapegoats, on which they can lay the blame of their own inadvertencies; well knowing, that, whatever may happen amiss, the young men will always have the specious excuse of using the name of government with respect to those acts which they may have reason to apprehend were devised by one man.

The Secretary of State

Gravity is the exterior of wisdom – what the body is to the mind; and, therefore, a principal secretary of state should always be a very grave man, for the world is greatly influenced in its opinion by appearances: but there is no necessity to enforce the axiom by argument. Something in the genius of so great an office as that of any one of his majesty's principal secretaries, instinctively inspires the requisite solemnity. The man is naturally so impressed with the honour to which he is called when raised to the office, that he becomes very complacent towards himself, and secretly thinks that there must surely be some thing paramount about him in the eyes of others (though he himself, for the life of him, cannot discover in what it consists), that he inevitably becomes grave and magisterial.

The difference between a principal and an under-secretary of state is not very recondite; the latter is only a more responsible servant: for it is a curious fact, that the higher the office the less is the responsibility. The apex of a pyramid is a point; and, for the same reason, the king can do no wrong.

It has been found, that the reflections of men are wise and comprehensive in proportion to the pressure of responsibility upon their intellects; just as atmospheric air expands in the receiver as it is exhausted. A smaller quantity of mind serves in certain high places than in those of the common walks of life, but it is not always prudent to declare this esoteric doctrine to the public.

We never hear nowadays of kings chopping off the heads of their secretaries, as they did in ancient times; but this does not arise from any additional value which the heads may have acquired: in truth, it has been long supposed that secretaries have not improved. I can aver, however, that when I was secretary of state the popular opinion was not quite correct on this subject.

But although gravity is a most essential quality in a secretary of state, I do not say it ought to be considered as the first; for I am taught by experience to believe, that a judicious contempt for popular opinion is highly efficacious. It would never, indeed, do, that those around whom every fence of the constitution is drawn should not have it in their power to act just as they pleased, however much policy may require that they are seen as superior men. But, as I have said, in in speaking of the more responsible officers – the under-secretaries of state – their chief duty is to keep themselves from being mixed up with transactions, the issue of which is uncertain; and for this reason, they should always appear to be actuated by information diametrically opposite to the facts known to the public. And, to do this effectually, they must select men to fill offices wholly on account of their interest; because, being appointed for that reason to offices, the salaries of which are the most suitable, they are the more likely to receive accounts at variance with public opinion. No doubt this sometimes leads to inconvenience, especially if there happen to be a party interested in the case, and who knows the subject more thoroughly than the officer. The secretary having, however, derived his information from the official organ, can easily plead an excuse on that score; when, by contradiction, he cannot equivocate with the unintentional delusion to which, from the nature of things, he is liable.

The Premier

When I was prime minister, it was the custom to regard the sovereign in a strict constitutional light, with reference to the maxim that he can do no wrong. Accordingly, I did all in my power to make him a perfect cipher, and to lead him as little as possible into temptation. When I saw him intent to accomplish any object for the public good, I set my face against it; which induced him to ask support from his friends, who were never very cordially mine: and when he had done so, then I gave in reluctantly, as it might appear. By this address, I neutralised his and their opposition to measures of my own; for when they saw with what reluctance I had seemingly assented to their measures, they could not refuse assent to mine. Thus, I drew over to me those who were generally the king's friends, and his protectors against the machinations of ministers.

But there is a card much more difficult to play well in the hands of a premier than even the king – the ace; or, in other words, the people: for whatever turns out contrary to public expectation, is immediately imputed by the popular voice to the minister. I do not mean him in whose department the accident happens, but the pilot of affairs.

After much serious reflection, I contrived to keep the public attention fixed on the special duties of each department; and thus, in whichever the fault arose, the minister of that department was obliged to answer for it to the people, though he might have had nothing to do either with the origin or development of the matter in question: for the bulk of the people do not know that a member of the cabinet is only responsible, as a minister, for what shall have appeared to be the sense of the cabinet. The minister in whose department the execution of a measure may lie, may have been in the minority when it was determined on in council, and it is not in human nature to expect that a minister can be very hearty in the execution of a cause to which he was inimical.

It is not, however, very easy to account for men remaining in office, after measures have failed which they resisted in the previous discussion, and to the failure of which, from the perversity of human nature, they perhaps contributed; nevertheless, it is so, and men climb into higher trusts: for, when a measure which they opposed when first agitated turns out to be ill-fated, they generally contrive some way of directing the popular indignation against the true parent, and thereby exonerate themselves, even when the evil destiny of the measure may have taken its colouring from their own secret wish that it might not succeed.

But some men are so fond of place, that they will remain in it at all hazards; and thus it happens, that governments of distinguished weakness are often, by the subserviency of these men to the unknown power behind the throne, seemingly wiser and more judicious than administrations of larger calibre. But, although this must be admitted, it is not without its advantages; for it is commonly supposed, that a man who has been long in office, and with different parties, must have profited by his experience, although the real cause of his adhesion to the place was in the importance to him of the salary.

If these slight cursory hints are wisely considered, which I have, with as much brevity as is consistent with perspicuity, endeavoured to put together, few statesmen ordained to occupy the vantage ground of national circumstances but must find them fraught with utility and instruction.

NOTES

The Mem, or Schoolmistress

Galt's subtitle ('From the Papers of the late Rev. Micah Balwhither, of Dalmailing') indicates that this story was written as a postscript to the *Annals*. There are clear signs that he has envisaged the story not in 'Dalmailing' but in Irvine: in Miss Peerie's town, the houses are entered through a 'close', there is a 'Green', and the young men go to sea on Virginia traders. It was published in *Fraser's Magazine* in August 1834 and was probably part of the 'trunkful' of manuscripts referred to in the following note. It was printed as 'By John Galt'.

The Gudewife

This was published ('By the author of "Annals of the Parish" ') in *Fraser's Magazine* in December 1833. There is a jocular preface by the editor ('Oliver Yorke', i.e. W. Maginn) recounting a visit he paid to Galt at Barn Cottage in Brompton. The account is clearly exaggerated well beyond credibility: Maginn writes that he secured a 'trunkful' of manuscripts from Galt, paid him a hundred guineas, and resold them to Fraser for five hundred guineas. One can accept the visit as genuine but not the details. Galt had just completed a three-volume gathering of stories for his *Stories of the Study*, which was published in November 1833. It is likely that Maginn's 'trunkload' consisted only of *The Mem* and *The Gudewife*.

The Seamstress

This was printed in *Stories of the Study*, 1833. Many of the stories in that collection, which Galt put together for the publishers Cochrane and McCrone to raise money to enable his two older sons to settle in Canada, consisted of old material that Galt had not been able to have published. But he included three Scottish stories, all recent work, *The Seamstress*, *The Dean of Guild* and *The Jaunt*, each of them a variation of the short story genre which he had begun to develop. *The Seamstress* is set in Irvine. In most of his work he had disguised his birthplace as 'Gudetown' or 'Garnock' or 'Dozent' but here he mentions the town by name. His short introduction has been retained. This critical statement, along with the 'Postscript by the Author' in volume three of *Ringan Gilhaize*, sets out Galt's artistic justification for his use of Scots.

The Publisher

On Galt's death in 1839, his widow went to join her three sons, who were all at that date in Canada. She took with her Galt's entire collection of manuscript material, which included some 1600 sheets of literary manuscript, mainly of poems and stories. The collection is now in the Public Archives of Canada in Ottawa. The three chapters of *The Publisher* is printed from Galt's manuscript, by courtesy of the Public Archives. It forms the first three chapters of an unfinished 'autobiography' which are shapely enough to stand by themselves.

In *The Publisher*, Galt once again returns to Irvine. The book-seller's shop, in which Robin Thrive learns the elements of his trade, is 'forenent the Trone' – along Irvine ('Dozent') High Street, not very far away from the shop of Mr Pawkie, the hero of *The Provost*. Galt's ironical study of Robin Thrive is based on his own experience of his publishers, William Blackwood (who is here fitted out with a West of Scotland origin) and of Colburn and Bentley, for whom Galt recorded that he worked 'like an upholsterer'. Authors, to Galt's fictional publisher, were merely 'operators of the literary manufactory'.

The work can be dated with some precision. Chapter 1 and 2 are in Galt's clear handwriting of 1832. By the end of that year his handwriting was affected by his stroke and he used his son Alexander as an amanuenis. The third chapter is in Alexander's schoolboy hand. Galt made no attempt to expand beyond the three chapters. Blackwood's death in 1834 made that impossible. But he carefully preserved the manuscript, and it is published in book form for the first time. See also: Ian A. Gordon 'Three New Chapters by John Galt', *Scottish Literary Journal*, 3:1 (1976), 23–30.

Our Borough

Our Borough was written in 1832 and submitted to William Blackwood, who published the first three chapters (without indication of authorship, not even the usual 'Author of *Annals* etc.') in *Blackwood's Magazine* in October 1832. Galt, now ill, dictated a continuation, but Blackwood wrote that he was 'disappointed in these last chapters' and returned them. Galt, in his usual economical way, set the rejected material aside, and it was to become the basis for *The Dean of Guild* which he included in his *Stories of the Study*, 1833.

Galt had completed in 1831–2 his two political novels *The Member* and *The Radical*, both set in London. His earlier novel, *The Provost* of 1822, had been a study of a small-town politician in his native Irvine. Galt intended

Our Borough to combine the two worlds. But Blackwood's refusal of the continuation was wise. The three chapters he published was a unified piece of work, an admirable study of small-town politics, the minor Machiavellis perturbed by London news of Reform and the threat of a Whig government.

The Dean of Guild

In the first printing of *Our Borough*, the only author assigned was 'the Dean of Guild'. *Our Borough* concluded with the Dean of Guild finding that he has been sent on a one-man deputation to London to spy out the best course of action for a Tory town council landed with a Whig administration in the Capital. Blackwood's rejection of the continuation proved a blessing in disguise. It gave time for Galt to think again. He rewrote his material and expanded it into *The Dean of Guild*, which he included in *Stories of the Study* 1833. The country cousin in the great city was a theme he always managed with skill. In *The Ayrshire Legatees* of 1821 and *The Gathering of the West* of 1823 he had contrived to wring both humour and humanity from the Ayrshire countrymen, when they were confronted by the great events of the day in either London or Edinburgh. It was a formula that could be put to work again. Galt's Dean of Guild, Mr Wamle, is a nice blend of country innocence and small-town cunning ('pawkiness' is the untranslatable Scots word) who measures the mighty with his home-bred standards. A man who can be awakened by the bells of Westminster and hear 'the town-clock in the neighbouring Abbey chap seven' will take a shrewd, indeed canny, look at even the Great Duke.

Galt, aware that on occasion his realism had misfired, carefully dissociated himself (in a long postscript which I have not reprinted) from Mr Wamle's political assessments. He need not have worried. When he came in 1834 to publish his *Literary Life*, he was able to print, among his list of subscribers, His Grace the Duke of Wellington.

His formula had been successful once again. So successful, that Galt decided to repeat it. He wrote, for *Stories of the Study*, a long travelogue. Mr Wamle (he has now become Mr Daidles) loses his office in the political upset that followed on the events of 1832. In *The Jaunt* Galt sends him and his wife on an extended tour of Europe (repeating much of the journey that Galt himself had done between 1809 and 1813 – Galt wasted nothing). It is a comic trip, but unfortunately extended beyond the space limits of the present volume.

The Howdie

The Howdie was published in the September and October 1833 issues of *Tait's Edinburgh Magazine*. The journal, established in April of that year, was edited by Mrs Christian Isobel Johnstone, an old admirer of Galt's talent. She had been responsible, in May of 1821, for the first review of *Annals of the Parish* that had acclaimed that book's quality; and her continued support of Galt was to provide him with his main outlet for publication in his final years, after the death of William Blackwood in 1834. Tait invited Galt to send a contribution in his own 'peculiar style' and Galt responded with the two parts of *The Howdie*, the autobiography of a midwife. It was writing of this sort that had led Blackwood, Dr Moir and Susan Ferrier to deplore Galt's 'vulgarity'. Mrs Johnstone was of different mettle. She enjoyed it, and in her own novel *West Coast Exclusives* (printed in *Tait's Edinburgh Magazine* 1834–5) one of her characters has 'a fancy for vulgarians' and openly praises 'Galt's vulgar, *outré*, characters'.

The Howdie appeared in the magazine without any attribution to Galt. Galt's letters to Tait (which are now in the National Library of Scotland and in the University of Edinburgh library) leave no doubt about the authorship. The manuscript of part I is in the N.L.S. It was edited in 1923 by W. Roughead. The present edition is the first reprinting of the full text of *The Howdie*.

Tribulations of the Rev. Cowal Kilmun

This novella-length story was offered by Galt to Tait in August 1835 as 'after the manner of *Annals of the Parish*'; Galt describes it accurately as 'an odd but common train of incidents'. It was published ('by John Galt') in *Tait's Edinburgh Magazine*, November and December 1835 and January 1836. The name of the narrator appeared in the first number as 'Conal' but was corrected thereafter both in the headnotes and the text to 'Cowal'. In spite of Galt's comparison with the *Annals*, the Rev. Cowal Kilmun is a very different figure from the downright and shrewd Rev. Micah Balwhidder of Dalmailing. Dalmailing is a Scottish lowland parish. Both Cowal and Kilmun are Argyllshire place-names. The Rev. Cowal Kilmun has a Highland parish, on one of the sea-lochs across the Clyde from Greenock, a setting familiar to Galt from his stay in Finnart on Loch Long in 1818. One of the recurring words in this story is 'mystical'. Galt (cf. his Mrs Edie in *The Entail*) always associated the Highlands with forebodings and second-sight. Kilmun's experiences (though expressed in Galt's Lowland Scots) are of the mysterious side of life.

The period is that of the *Annals*, the late eighteenth century. Galt's details are, as ever, unobtrusive, but accurate: America has declared its independence (1776) and the journey from London to Leith is not by James Watt's steamer but by sail on the 'smack'. The strange power of this story undoubtedly springs from its unconscious symbolism. There are no minor characters. The three central figures are all aspects of Galt. Mr Roslin is the returned colonial emigrant. Mr Ettles is the failed man of affairs – when Galt was in Canada, his coach bore the motto 'I ettle' ('I strive'). The Rev. Cowal Kilmun and his sister

Becky parallel Galt's own situation in Greenock after 1834, living quietly in the old family house with his sister. The turmoil of life was, for both the creator and his creation, separated by time and distance – it is, in a constantly recurring phrase – 'across the ferry'.

A Rich Man

This story was written in 1835–6 and was offered to *Blackwood's Magazine* and refused. The sons of William Blackwood had no great opinion of their father's discovery of 1820. It appeared in the June, July and August issues of *Tait's Edinburgh Magazine* 1836, under the more appreciative eye of Mrs Johnstone. It was announced as 'By John Galt'. In this story – it is possibly Galt's finest piece of writing in the vernacular – Galt returns to the theme of *The Member* and *Sir Andrew Wylie*, the lad who from humble beginnings conquers the greater London world. Archibald Plack has been Lord Mayor of London but he has lost none of his Scots speech; and his autobiography, told in a series of letters to his spendthrift grandson ('George Spend') shows Galt at his vernacular and ironic best.

The Statesman

The Statesman, reprinted here for the first time since its first appearance in *Fraser's Magazine* of December 1836, was the last of Galt's stories to be published in his lifetime. Galt returns to the world of *The Member*, of which *The Statesman* is a witty and tightly-written variation. The story is cast in the form of a mocking and ironic manual on the manipulation of political power.

ANNOTATIONS AND VOCABULARY

a': all
aboon: above
ae: one
aff-set: offspring
aiblins: perhaps
ain: own
airt: direction
ajee: awry
alloo: allow
all-overish: out of sorts
among hands: incidentally
anent: concerning
arcana: secrets
arle, erle: earnest, pledge
art and part: (Scots law) party to
ashypet: a 'Cinderella', a dirty neglected child
assoilyied: acquitted
aught: anything
auld daddie: grandfather
auld-farrant: sagacious
auld langsyne: times gone by
awmous: alms
aye: always
ayont: beyond

bairn: child
baith: both
bardy: pert
barley: truce (Fr. *parler*)
barm: ferment
barming: brewing, 'increase'
baudrons: 'pussy-cat'
bawbee: small coin
baxter: baker
begane: begone
behoof: behalf
bein: wealthy
bell: bubble
Beltane: 1st of May
ben: inner room; (adv.) within
ben, far: 'well in', advanced, successful
besom: broom
Besom: (Lord) Brougham (pronounced 'broom')
betherel: beadle, gravedigger
between hands: meantime
bide: stay (at)
big: dig
biggen: grow big, increase
bir, birr: vigour
birkie: lively fellow
birses: bristles, 'anger'
birsle: scorch
bit: (adj.) little
blate: bashful
blattering: lashing (of rain)
blaw: blow
blinks: gleams
blithesmeat: food prepared for visitors at child's birth
bock: retch, vomit
bodie: person
bodle: small coin
body, out of the: crazy
bonnet laird: small landholder
bouk: body, trunk of body
boun: ready
bout: behoved
boutger: glutton
bowet: hand lantern

bowit: bowed, bent
brae: hill
braid: broad
brawly: bravely
bray: (vb.) squeeze, pound
breeks: trousers
briz: bruise, pound (e.g. in mortar)
brod: 'board', plate (orig. wooden) for holding church collection
broo: favour
broo, have no: have no favourable opinion (of)
Broomielaw: wharf district in Glasgow on river Clyde
bruizer: 'bruiser', pestle
bubbly-jock: turkey
buckie, roaring: unruly child
buck nor, stie: (vbl. phrs.) do neither one thing or the other
buirdly: stalwart
burn: stream
butt: target (archery)
by common: out of the common, unusual
bygone: past
by-hand: casual; settled; disposed of
by himself, themselves etc: crazy
by ordinary: beyond the ordinary
by-set: setting aside
byke: nest (esp. of insects), house
byke, skail the: disperse the assembly

ca': drive
ca' canny: go carefully
cadies: cadets (in East India Company)
cagie, caidgy: sportive, gay
callant: lad
calm sough, keep a: keep quiet
camstrary: unmanageable
cankry: ill-humoured
cannily: prudently
canny: careful, prudent
canny, ca': go carefully
canny, no: (adj.) odd, strange
carl: fellow
carline, carlin: old woman
carritch: question
Carritches, Mother's: elementary form of presbyterian shorter catechism, *The Mother's Catechism*, 1758
carry't: 'carried away', distraught
cauk: chalk, talc
causey: street (causeway)
cess: tax
chack: snack (of food)
chandler pins: spikes on which candles were set
chandler pins, on: spruced up; proud (cf. 'stuck up')
chap: knock, make a sound
cheeping: chirping (of birds)
choppin: quart
chucky-stone: pebble
chumly: chimney
chumly lug: fireside
churm: murmur
circumbendibus: (joc.) tumble
clachan: village
claes: clothes
clanjamfry: rabble
clau': clause
claw: scratch
cleading, cleeding: clothing
clecking: hatching
clock, clok: hatch
close, closs: narrow tunnel-like entry to a building
close-mouth: the opening to a close
clouts: pieces of cloth; baby-clothes
clutes, cloots: cloven hooves
cod: pillow, cushion
cog, cogie: bowl
coggle: shake, joggle
coggliness, instability, shaky state
coggly: unstable, shaky

cognosce: scrutinise
cold-rife: cold
collegeners: students
common, by: unusual, out of the common
condescending: polite, 'civil'
concos mentis: crazy (*non compos mentis*)
confabble: discuss
connek: connected, close
constipated: (joc.) confused
coomy: dirty
corbies: crows
corky-headed: giddy, light-headed
corruption: anger
coupit: overturned
couthy: agreeable, pleasant, kind
Coutts, Tommy: founder of bank, Coutts and Co.
covenanted: agreed
crack: talk, chat
craft: croft, small-holding; skill
craig: neck
creeshy: greasy
cross, the: mercat cross in Scottish town. Hence 'town centre'. The site of the demolished cross in Glasgow was known as 'the cross' and was the commercial centre in the eighteenth century.
crouse: brave
crousely: bravely
cruise, crusie: oil lamp
crunkly: rough
cutty: wretch (of female – can be used pejoratively or affectionately, acc. to context)
cutty-crumb: 'small, cut-up, crumb', i.e. tiny, childish

daffin: sport, frolic
Dagon, darling: darling idol (not pejorative)
damas: damson
Damon and Phillising: courting (from names of Pastoral lovers)
dankle: deviate (from)
darg: work
daud: lash, drive forcibly
dauner: stroll
daunton: intimidate, tame
daur: dare
dawty: saucy (of a female)
dawty, my: my dear
deacon: expert
dead-ill: final illness
dead thraws: death throes
Dean of Guild: in the eighteenth century Scottish boroughs, this (lucrative) office ranked after the Provost and bailies, a stepping-stone to higher office
departal: departure
deval, devaul: refrain, cease (from)
dickey: rear (outside) seat in coach for servants
dirgie, draigie: funeral service, 'wake'
disjasked: worn-out
divor: bankrupt
doit: small coin
doited: stupid
donsie: saucy, silly
dooly: sadness
douce: sober, calm
doup: buttocks, rear end
dour, dure: stubborn, unsmiling
dover: snooze, light sleep
dowie: downcast
down-draught: something which drags a person down, impediment. Also pun with banking sense of 'draft' and 'drawing down' money
dozened: slowed-down, numb, sleepy
Dozent, borough of: i.e. Irvine (from *dozent:* sleepy). cf. 'Dozent is a sort of sleeping borough-town

and stands upon the toll-road' (Galt, *The Betheral*, p. 4)
draigie, dirgie: funeral wake
drappie: small drop (of spirits)
dreichly: drearily
drudger: dredger (of flour, powder)
duberous: raising doubts, dubious
duds: clothing
dule: grief
Dumbarton Youth: (trad. phrs.) anyone, male or female, over 36
dungeon of wit: intellectual person
dunkle: injure, 'dent'
dwam: swoon
dwine: decline
dyke: stone wall, field boundary

ee: eye
e'en: even
een: eyes
effigy: symbol
egg: incite
eildins, of an: of an equal age
elder: church elder
elshin: awl
ends and awls: 'bits and pieces' (metaph. from shoe making, *ends:* thread ends)
end's errant: errand with a single purpose
enfoeffment: (Scots law) possession
erls, arls: earnests, pledges
errander: message-boy
ettering: (lit. 'festering'), issue
ettle: strive
even: (vb.) equate
evendown: plain, downright
eydency, eidency: industry (see Galt's note on *The Seamstress*)
eydent, eident: industrious

faik: abate
fainness: pleasure
fairings: presents bought at a fair
Falkland Islands: in the late eighteenth century their ownership was disputed between Britain and Spain
fash: (vb.) trouble
fasherie: (n.) trouble
fashous: troublesome
fat: container (cf. 'vat'), in combin. 'salt-fat'
fause: false
feed: paid by regular wages (p.p. of vb. 'fee')
fen: (vb.) fend
fenn't: fended
ferley, ferlie: marvel
feuar: lease-holder
fiky: fussy, fastidious
firkin, firikin: keg
flaad: slab, sheet (of newspaper)
flabbing: showing, display
fleech: coax
flit: move, esp. move furniture to new house
fly: coach
flyting: abuse in words
foot, for a sore (sair): for an emergency
forbye, forebye: in addition
fore, to the: alive
forefoughten: wearied
forenent: opposite
fou, fu': drunk, 'full'
freat: superstition, omen
friend: close relation
frush: brittle
functi offishy: functus officii, dead
furthy: forward, unabashed
fyke: fidget, restlessness

gabbart: coastal vessel
gaed: went
gaen: gone
gaet, gate: road, way, manner
gair: covetous, keen, greedy

galravaging, galravitching: tumult, riotous living
Gamaliel: St. Paul was brought up 'at the feet of Gamaliel'; *Acts* 22, 3
gamaushins: gaiters
gang: go
gar: cause
gardevin: jar (for spirits)
garnel: granary
garnish: (adj.) 'polished'
gask: horror
gathering: savings (of money)
gauger: exciseman
gaunt: yawn
gavalling: riotous living
gawsy, gasy: portly, jolly
General Assembly: annual meeting of Church of Scotland
genty: elegant
geny: genius
get: child
gie: give
gied to my heart: struck to my heart
glaik: gleam
glaikit: silly
glebe: portion of land assigned to clergyman
gleg: sharp, bright
glint: glance
glunch: frown
go-bye, give the: avoid
go by oneself, himself etc: go crazy
Goose-dubs: 'The Goose Puddles', locality in eighteenth-century Glasgow
gotchard: grandfather
gowden: golden
gowl: howl, scold
gowpin, gowpen: handful
gradawa: physician ('graduate')
grat: wept
green: desire (vb.)
grumphie: pig
gude: good
gudeman, guidman: husband
gudewife, guidwife: wife
guess: riddle
gulbroch: ragwort
gumption: common sense

hain: save (money)
haivings: manners (from 'behavings')
Halloween: last night of October, before All Saints' Day
hame: home
hameart: 'homeward', at home, close at hand; homely
hands, among (atween): meantime
hand-waled: hand-picked, select
hanling: 'handling', manipulation; negotiation
hap: (vb.) cover; (n.) covering
harnish: harness
har'st: harvest; autumn
hauflin: half
haverel: idiot
havers: nonsense
heck: hay-rack
heck and manger, live at: feed without thought of cost (from cattle with free access to hay-rack and manger)
heckle: hackling-comb (for preparing flax for spinning)
hempie: rogue
hench: haunch
heritors: land-owners in a parish, responsible for upkeep of the local church
hesp: hasp (hank of yarn); lock
het: hot
het and fu': 'hot and full', (of a house) comfortable
hidling: secretive
hing: hang
hobbleshow: tumult

hoggart, hoggar: stocking; hence 'money saved up'
homolgomate: (joc.) establish
honesty: mark of repectability or station (used of 'good' clothing)
hooly: slowly
howdie: midwife
howff: snug shelter; place of meeting
howk: dig
huggars: wollen leggings
hussie-fellow: man who does woman's work
huxster: pedlar, trader
huxtry shop: general store

idleset: idleness
illess: innocent
ill-faurd: ill-favoured
imbreley: umbrella
income: sickness
Ingy: India
inns: inn
intil: into

jawp: dash (of water)
jealous, jalouse: suspect
jealousy: suspicion
jeopardy: adventure
jo: sweetheart
Jobbry: see *Mr Jobbry*
jocose: jolly
jook: dodge, avoid

kail-pot: soup-pot
kechle: cackle
ken: know
kenna-what: nondescript, 'so-and-so'
kenspeckle: conspicuous
kilfudyocking: fireside chat or disputation (the 'kilfuddie' was the aperture through which a kiln was fuelled; *yock:* talk; cf. 'yak')
killiree: (vb.) flaunt
Kilmarnock bonnet: 'Tam o' Shanter' bonnet
kingcost: whooping cough
kink: cough, choking
kirn: (vb.) grind, churn
kist: chest, coffin
kite: belly
kithe: appear, make plain
kitling: kitten, child
kittle: (vb. 1) produce young, increase
kittle: (vb. 2) tickle
kittle: (adj.) uncertain, tricky
kittly: itchy

laft: 'loft', raised place, gallery
lair: (1) learning
lair: (2) burial plot
laitheron: sloven
laive, lave: remainder
lamiter: crippled person
lampet: limpet
land: tall multi-storey tenement building (esp. Edinburgh and Glasgow)
lanely, lanerly: lonely
lap: leapt
latter days: Days of Judgment
leal: faithful
lees: lies
leet: (vb.) put on a list for election. In the eighteenth century self-perpetuating Scottish boroughs, to be leeted was tantamount to being appointed
Leven: tributary, joining river Clyde at Dumbarton
lift: sky
lines: in context, 'appointed lot'; from Psalm 16.6, 'The lines are fallen unto me in pleasant places'
lint: flax
logive: extravagant, careless

look-to: (n.) consideration
loot: bend down
loup: leap
loup-the-dyke: (adj.) 'leap-over-the wall', flighty
lovish: lavish
lown: calm
Luckie: 'Mistress' (of older women)
lug: ear
lum: chimney
lying money: savings

Manchester Buildings: set of bachelor apartments in Westminster, popular with M.P.s. Mr Jobbry (of *The Member*) lived there
manger: see *heck*
marrow: like; companion
maun: must
Meg Dorts: 'haughty Meg'; from Ramsay's *Gentle Shepherd*, I.i
megstie: Mighty! (exclam. of surprise)
meikle: much
melt: (from vb. *mell*) meddled with
messes or mells: mingles (*mess:* dine; *mell:* mingle (with)
Michaelmas: date for elections to eighteenth-century Scottish boroughs
midden: dung-heap
mim: prim, demure
minaway: minuet
mind: (vb.) remember
mint: (vb.) intend, aim, hint
misleared: unmannerly
mity powder: hair-powder contaminated by mites
molly-grubs: colic
morn, the: tomorrow
mort: corpse
moulin, moullen: crumb
Mr Jobbry: hero of Galt's *The Member*, referred to in *The Dean of Guild*
muckle: much
mudge: move
muslin kail: vegetable broth
mutch: cap (usually, but not exclusively, a woman's)
mutchkin: vessel (holding a pint)

naething: nothing
naggy: horse
native: new-born child
nawby: 'nabob', wealthy person
neb: nose, beak
ne'er begun, nearbegaun: niggardly
neive: fist
neuk: corner
new-light: 'New Lights', section of Presbyterian church
nicheringly: laughingly
niffer: exchange, swap
niggarality: niggardliness
no: (adj.) not; e.g. *no blate:* not bashful
nonplus, nonplush: surprised
nonplushed: surprised
nugger-mugger: hugger mugger, plot

obligatory: obliging
Occasion, the: sacrament of Communion
oe: grandchild
o'ercome: chorus or 'burden' of a song; theme
ony: any
operative: (n.) workman
opiatical: from *opiate*
ordinar, by: out of the ordinary
orthoxies: (joc.) orthodoxies
out: (vb.) expend
outing: expense, display
outfall: result, occurrence
outstropolous: obstreperous, outrageous

overly: (adv.) too, too much
overly dourly: too stubbornly
owre, ower: over; too

Pace-and-Yule dainty: delicacy made only at Easter and Christmas
packet: ship on regular run
paction: bargain
parafarnals, parapharnauly: woman's dress and ornaments
parethetical: parenthetical
Parish: Paris
parliament-cake: crisp gingerbread biscuit
pass-over: assuagement
pater-nostring: chatter, discussion
patron: pattern
pavý: pavement (Fr. *pavé*)
pawkie: sly
payway: valediction
peinor pig, penure pig: receptacle for savings; cf. 'piggy bank'
pelloch: porpoise
peoies: fireworks, made of moistened gunpowder
peremptors, on his: exacting, being very precise
perfect: absolute
perish the pack: squander everything
pickle: (adj.) few
pikerry: (Scots law) pilfering
placed: established as minister in a church
plack: small coin
plain-work: plain sewing
plane-stones: flagged pavement; in eighteenth-century Glasgow only in the centre by the Cross – the parade-ground of wealthy merchants
plant: hoard, deposit
playock: toy
playoc bairn: child at play
ploy: sport, business, manoeuvre
pluff-in-the-pan: flash in the pan
pock: bag
pock-nook (neuk): bottom or corner of a bag; hence 'resources'
poney cock: turkey
poopit: pulpit
pot-metal: cast-iron; base-metal (with sense of 'second-rate')
pouches: pockets
pourie: cream-jug
powter: (n.) raking action, poke
pree: taste
preeing: trial, tasting
prejinct, perjink: precise
prin: pin
provice: provost
public: (n.) inn, public house
puddock: frog
pue, play: (usually in negative) compete (with), match
puir: poor
Pumpington: (Duke of) Wellington
pyet: magpie

quiskoskos: doubtful
quiskous: quirky, unreliable

rambling: rough, boisterous
ramplor, ramplar: rowdy, boisterous
randy: (n.) scold
ravel: twist (of rope, flax etc.)
ravelment: tangle, quarrel
rax: (vb.) stretch
raxes: andirons
redd: (vb.) advise, counsel
Relief: the Relief Church, a presbyterian group which opposed the General Assembly of the church
retour: return
rib: wife (Adam's rib)
rickle: heap
rift: belch
ripe: probe

riping the ribs: poking the bars (of the grate)
rive: tear
rouse: high opinion, praise
routing: bellowing (of cattle)
Royal Georges: i.e. 'ships'
rug: (vb.) haul
runagate: unsettled; worthless
rung: staff (usually assoc. with beggar)

saft-horn: novice (cf. 'greenhorn')
Samaria: country of the Good Samaritan
sanctified . . . Abbey: Holyrood Abbey at the date was a sanctuary for debtors
sappy: juicy, 'profitable'
saulying: sallying
scad: reflection
sclate: slate
scog: (vb.) shelter, conceal
scomfished: stifled, exhausted
scowry: showery
scrutoire: desk
sec: sex
sederunt: (n.) session; (adj.) sitting
session: Kirk Session, church elders
shavelin-gabbit: sharp-tongued (*gab:* mouth; *shavelin:* spoke-shave)
shavlingly: smoothly (from 'shavelin')
shining: (from 'shin') moving
shirra, shirrif: sherrif
shortly: crossly, angrily
shune, shoon: shoes
sib: related
sic: such
siccar, sicker: sure, certain
siller: 'silver'; money
simmer and winter: 'summer and winter'; needlessly spin out a narrative
sinsyne: since then
sixpence: child's reward for reciting Catechism
skail: disperse
skimmer: flicker, shimmer
slaik, slake: lick; touch, smattering
sliddiness: slippery nature
slipping: gentle
smeddum: spirit, vigour
smir, smur: (n. and vb.) drizzle
snod: (vb.) tidy
snodness: neatness
sonsy: plump, good-looking
soop, soup: sweep
sore foot, for a: for an emergency
sough: noise of wind; rumour
sough, keep a calm: keep quiet
souple: (adj.) cunning
soupleness: flexibility; cunning
souter: shoesmaker
sowans: oatmeal siftings boiled in water
sparing: (from *spare*: save) small savings of money
speant: fed with a spoon
speed: success
speir: enquire, ask a question, propose marriage
speshy: species
splore: (n.) frolic (which leads to meanings 'drinking-bout', fight)
spring: lively tune
sprose: (vb.) boast
sprose: (n.) boast, show
spunk: spark
stages: stage coaches
stang: sting, sharp pain
staun: stand, market-stall
stends: bruises
stern: star
stey, stye: steep
steybrae: steep hill
sticket minister: theological student who has failed to graduate

stie: see *buck*
stoiter: totter
stot: (vb.) bounce
stot: (n.) young bull or ox
stoup: (n.) prop
stoury: dusty
straemash: tumult, disturbance
stray: stroll
stroup: spout
swatch: piece of cloth, sample
sweert: reluctant

talons: talents
tan hole: tan-pit
tappy-tourock: (n.) top-knot; (adj.) elevated. Also punning ref. to turrets of 'Scottish Baronial' style of building
tavert: confused
teetle: title
tent, take: take heed
their: occasional spelling of *thir:* these
thole: endure
thrang, throng: busily engaged
thraws: throws
thrift: work, employment
tick, on: on credit
tierce: cask
timber-tuned: with no ear for music
tine: lose
tinkler: tinker, vagrant
tinselers: (Scots law) offenders
toll-road: in context, 'road outside city limits'. In the eighteenth century there was a toll-bar house at each exit from Glasgow
Tontine: Tontine Hotel in commercial centre of Glasgow, built 1784. The coffee-house was a haunt of wealthy merchants
too-look: expectation
toom: empty
topping: successful, wealthy
tot: sum
tout: toot
tow: flax
track-pot: tea-pot
trader: trading vessel
trintlet: trundled
Trongate: in the eighteenth century the commercial centre of Glasgow
turnpike-stair: winding staircase giving access to flats ('houses') in tenement buildings in Glasgow and Edinburgh
Twilight: i.e. (Earl) Grey
tympathy: morbid swelling

unco: (n.) strange thing; (adj.) strange; (adv.) very
up-cast: (n.) turn-up, result
uppings: pretentions
upsetting: ambitious, pretentious
upshot: (n.) outcome

vekle: vehicle
virgos: verjuice, acid juice of unripe fruit
vogie: cheerful; vain

wadset: (n.) mortgage
wae: (adj.) sorry
waeful: sorrowful
wakerife: wakeful
wally-draigle: the feeblest bird in a nest; often used metaphorically
wally-wallying: lamentation; lamenting
wark: work
warsle: wrestle, struggle
wastry: waste
wauken: waken
waur: (adj.) worse
waur, ware: (v.) spend
wean: small child
weel: well

well-faured: well-favoured, good-looking
wersh: insipid
wester: to the west of
whamle: tumble, invert
wheel: (often) 'spinning-wheel'
whilk: which
whiles: sometimes, at times
whins: gorse bushes
whinstone: basalt
whisk: sudden slight motion
whisky: gig (wheeled vehicle)
wice-like, wise-like: prudent
wile: entice
windlestrae: withered stalk of grass
wisdom bag: 'lucky bag'; lucky dip
wise: (vb.) direct
woo': wool
wrack and carry: cloud movements
writer: usually 'lawyer'; but sometimes in sense of 'author'
wynd: narrow lane or street
wyte: (n. and vb.) blame

yawp: hungry ('agape')
yeard tead: toad; lit. 'earth toad'
yedication: education
yett: gate
youky: itchy

Peacock